Pre-Algebra

Written by
Wendy Osterman

Editor: Alaska Hults
Illustrator: Corbin Hillam
Designer/Production: Moonhee Pak/Cari Helstrom
Cover Designer: Barbara Peterson
Art Director: Tom Cochrane
Project Director: Carolea Williams

Table of Contents

Introduction

Each book in the *Power Practice*™ series contains dozens of ready-to-use activity pages to provide students with skill practice. The fun activities can be used to supplement and enhance what you are already teaching in your classroom. Give an activity page to students as independent class work, or send the pages home as homework to reinforce skills taught in class. An answer key is included at the end of each book for verification of student responses.

Pre-Algebra provides activities that will directly assist students in practicing basic skills and concepts. The structure of the book enhances student learning and enables them to meet new challenges with confidence. Students will receive reinforcement in the following skills:
• determining divisibility
• finding common factors and multiples
• terminating and repeating decimals
• understanding integers and absolute value
• multiplying and dividing fractions
• finding and using percents
• using the order of operations
• finding the value of a given variable
• identifying and solving a monomial, binomial, or trinomial

Use these ready-to-go activities to "recharge" skill review and give students the power to succeed.

Number Chat

> **Set:** A collection of objects.
> **Whole Numbers:** The set of numbers that can be used to count, starting with 0.
> **Fraction:** Part of a whole number.
> **Decimal:** A number with one or more digits to the right of the decimal number.
> **Digit:** A single number. There are 10 digits: 0, 1, 2, 3, 4, 5, 6, 7, 8, and 9.

Write *whole number*, *fraction*, or *decimal* to indicate which would best represent the value.

1 The percent on a test _____

2 The number of students in the class _____

3 The part of the world that is made up of water _____

4 The cost to fill up a tank of gas _____

5 Half of an hour _____

6 The number of televisions in your house _____

7 The measurement in a recipe that is less than 1 full cup _____

8 The interest rate at a bank _____

9 The number of steps to get to school _____

10 The exact number of miles to the closest store _____

11 Baseball batting averages _____

12 Part of the pizza left after you eat your share _____

Naming Number Sets

Natural Numbers: The set of numbers that you use to count, starting with 1.

Integers: The set of all whole numbers, both positive and negative. {. . . , ⁻3, ⁻2, ⁻1, 0, 1, 2, 3, . . .}

Rational Numbers: The set of all integers plus all of the terminating or repeating decimals between the whole numbers.

Irrational Numbers: The set of all numbers that are not rational. If a number is not rational, then it must be irrational.

Write a number that fits the description.

1 I am an integer that is one less than 0. _____

2 I am a rational number that is between 3 and 4. _____

3 I am an integer that is between 0 and ⁻5. _____

4 I am a rational number that is one less than $\frac{1}{2}$. _____

5 I am both a rational number and a natural number that is between 58 and 60. _____

6 I am an integer that is 2 less than ⁻3. _____

7 I am a natural number that is 5 times greater than 2. _____

Write *natural number*, *integer*, *rational number*, or *irrational number* to indicate which would best respresent the value.

8 I am a decimal that does not terminate or repeat. _____

9 I am a number that is 2.5 more than 0.5. _____

10 I am a number that is 3.2 less than ⁻4. _____

11 I am a number that is 4 times greater than 1.25. _____

12 I am a number that is the product of two rational numbers. _____

Pre-Algebra © 2004 Creative Teaching Press

Math Operations

> **Sum:** The answer to an addition problem.
> **Difference:** The answer to a subtraction problem.
> **Product:** The answer to a multiplication problem.
> **Quotient:** The answer to a division problem.

Write an equation that illustrates the problem and solve it.

1 To find the area of a square, find the product of the length and the width.

_____

2 To find the average daily pay, find the quotient of the weekly pay, $350, and the number of days in a week.

_____

3 To find the discount, find the difference between the regular price of $30 and the discounted price of $22.

_____

4 Find the sum of all the baskets scored in the ball game. Only 10 players scored. The scores are 10, 20, 14, 13, 30, 12, 24, 4, 2, 3.

_____

5 Find the sum and the difference of the numbers 50 and 25.

_____

6 Find the product of the even integers in the set: {1, 2, 3, 4, 5, 6}.

_____

7 To find the square of the number 6, take the product of the number multiplied by itself.

_____

8 To find the remainder of 36 divided by 5, find the difference of 36 and the product of 5 and 7.

_____

Vocabulary Practice

Review

For each given definition or set of numbers, circle the best vocabulary word.

1 {. . . , ⁻3, ⁻2, ⁻1, 0, 1, 2, 3, . . .}

    Whole   Naturals   Integers   Rationals   Irrationals

2 {0, 1, 2, 3, . . .}

    Whole   Naturals   Integers   Rationals   Irrationals

3 {1, 2, 3, . . .}

    Whole   Naturals   Integers   Rationals   Irrationals

4 This is the set of all integers plus all of the terminating or repeating decimals between the whole numbers.

    Whole   Naturals   Integers   Rationals   Irrationals

5 A collection of objects

    Digits   Fractions   Set   Sum

6 {1, 2, 3, 4, 5, 6, 7, 8, 9}

    Whole   Naturals   Integers   Rationals   Digits

7 Part of a whole number

    Decimals   Digits   Fraction   Difference

8 The answer to an addition problem

    Sum   Difference   Product   Quotient   Divisible

9 The answer to a multiplication problem

    Sum   Difference   Product   Quotient   Divisible

10 The answer to a subtraction problem

    Sum   Difference   Product   Quotient   Divisible

11 The answer to a division problem

    Sum   Difference   Product   Quotient   Divisible

Pre-Algebra © 2004 Creative Teaching Press

Crossword

R E V I E W

Use the clues to complete the puzzle.

Across

2. The set of all numbers that are not rational.
4. Part of a whole number.
6. The answer to a division problem.
9. This is the set: {. . . , ⁻3, ⁻2, ⁻1, 0, 1, 2, 3, . . .}
11. The answer to a multiplication problem.
12. A number with one or more digits to the right of the decimal point.
13. The answer to an addition problem.

Down

1. The answer to a subtraction problem.
3. The set of all integers plus all of the terminating or repeating decimals.
5. The set of numbers that can be used to count starting with 0.
7. The set of numbers that you use to count starting with 1.
8. Single numbers from 0 to 9.
10. A collection of objects.

Name _____ Date _____

Clue Words

Add	Subtract	Multiply	Divide
Tally Count up	Deduct Take away	Grow Magnified	Partition Breaking up

For each operation brainstorm additional clue words that are found in math word problems.

1) Add

_____

_____

_____

_____

_____

2) Subtract

_____

_____

_____

_____

_____

3) Multiply

_____

_____

_____

_____

4) Divide

_____

_____

_____

_____

Pre-Algebra © 2004 Creative Teaching Press

Looking for Clues

Circle the clue words and write the operation below the word.

1 Mr. Fred needs to tally up his minutes to see if he has any more minutes to use on his phone card.

2 The sale price of the radio is $20 less than the regular price.

3 The photo size was magnified by 3.

4 You expect the total sales for the video store to be 500 videos more than last year.

5 The wall needs to be partitioned into 4-foot sections and the number of 4-foot sections needs to be counted with the other three walls.

6 Rachel's mom is going to deduct her allowance from the cost of the sweater she wants.

7 Morgan is going to take 5 pieces of candy from the jar.

8 The kids needed an extra 20 minutes to shop at the mall.

9 The store clerk needs to count all of the money in her drawer except the money that was there when she started working.

Using Clue Words

Choose one of the following activities to complete in the space below.

- Using some of your own "clue words," write some story problems of your own.
- Look in books, magazines, and newspapers to find some text that uses clue words. Cut and paste your examples or copy the sentences to the space below.

Pre-Algebra © 2004 Creative Teaching Press

Looking for Remainders

Evenly Divisible: The quotient of two numbers is a whole number.
16 is evenly divisible by 2 because 16 ÷ 2 = 8 (a whole number)
16 is not divisible by 3 because 16 ÷ 3 = 5.$\overline{3}$ (not a whole number)

Solve.

1 Is 36 evenly divisible by 6?

_____

2 Is 48 evenly divisible by 9?

_____

3 Is 1,204 evenly divisible by 2?

_____

4 Is 345 evenly divisible by 8?

_____

5 Is 678 evenly divisible by 3?

_____

6 Is 198 evenly divisible by 9?

_____

7 Is 1,250 evenly divisible by 10?

_____

8 Is 589 evenly divisible by 6?

_____

9 Is 276 evenly divisible by 4?

_____

10 Is 548 evenly divisible by 3?

_____

11 Is 1,296 evenly divisible by 6?

_____

12 Is 6 evenly divisible by 36?

_____

Divisibility Tests

A natural number is divisible by…

2 if the number is even.
3 if the sum of the digits is divisible by 3.
4 if the number formed by its last two digits is divisible by 4.
5 if the last digit is a 5 or a 0.
6 if the number is divisible by both 2 and 3.
8 if the number formed by the last three digits is divisible by 8.
9 if the sum of the digits is divisible by 9.
10 if the last digit is a 0.

Example:
Is 98,536 divisible by 2, 3, 4, 5, 6, 8, 9, 10?

2 Yes, because it is even.
3 No, because 9 + 8 + 5 + 3 + 6 = 31, which is not divisible by three.
4 Yes, because 36 is divisible by 4.
5 No, because it doesn't end in a 5 or a 0.
6 No, because it is only divisible by 2 and not by 3.
8 Yes, because 536 is divisible by 8 (536 ÷ 8 = 67).
9 No, because 9 + 8 + 5 + 3 + 6 = 31, which is not divisible by nine.
10 No, because it doesn't end in a 0.

Determine if the following numbers are divisible by 2, 3, 4, 5, 6, 8, 9, and 10.

1 1,008 _____

2 3,024 _____

3 1,920 _____

4 518,400 _____

5 186,624 _____

6 319,599 _____

In the following exercises, find the number(s) that make each statement true.

7 | 2 | 3 | 5, | 1 | 3 | | is divisible by the number 2.

8 | 6 | 7 | 8, | | 1 | 0 | is divisible by the number 3.

9 | 3 | 4, | 5 | 6 | 8, | 7 | | 8 | is divisible by the number 8.

10 | 3 | 4 | 6, | 1 | 3 | | is divisible by the number 4.

Factors

A **factor** is a whole number that is multiplied by another whole number to equal a product.

Factors of 24: 1, 2, 3, 4, 6, 8, 12, and 24

List all of the factors for each number.

1 42

_____

2 77

_____

3 210

_____

4 126

_____

5 50

_____

6 200

_____

7 143

_____

8 58

_____

9 61

_____

10 89

_____

Common Factors

Common Factor: A number that is a factor of two or more numbers.

Common factors of 12 and 24: 2, 3, 4, 6, and 12

Find the common factors of each set of numbers.

1) 42
77

_____

2) 16
36

_____

3) 81
63

_____

4) 19
23

_____

5) 43
97

_____

6) 20
48

_____

7) 40
56

_____

8) 49
70

_____

9) 100
50

_____

10) 36
24

_____

Pre-Algebra © 2004 Creative Teaching Press

Greatest Common Factor

Greatest Common Factor (GCF): The common factor of two or more numbers that has the greatest value.
The GCF of 12 and 24 is 12.

Hint: The GCF will never be larger than the smallest number of the set.
The GCF of 4 and 4,000,000 is 4.

Find the GCF of each set of numbers.

1 42 and 77

_____

2 210 and 126

_____

3 42, 77, 210, and 126

_____

4 86, 129, and 215

_____

5 17, 43, and 83

_____

6 25, 30, and 50

_____

7 30 and 75

_____

8 27 and 12

_____

9 19 and 95

_____

10 33 and 180

_____

Pre-Algebra © 2004 Creative Teaching Press

Multiples

> **Multiple:** The product of a number and a whole number.
> Some multiples of 12 are 12, 24, 36, and 48.
> **Common Multiple:** A number that is a multiple of two or more numbers.
> Some common multiples of 12 and 24 are 24, 48, and 72.
> **Least Common Multiple (LCM):** The multiple common to two or more numbers with the least value.
> The LCM of 12 and 24 is 24.

Follow the directions for each problem.

1 List the first 10 multiples of the number 5. _____

2 List the first 10 multiples of the number 6. _____

3 List three common multiples of the numbers 5 and 6. _____

4 What is the LCM of the numbers 5 and 6? _____

5 List the first 10 multiples of the number 7. _____

6 List the first 10 multiples of the number 14. _____

7 List three common multiples of the numbers 7 and 14. _____

8 What is the LCM of the numbers 7 and 14? _____

Name _____ Date _____

Factors and Multiples

A **factor** will never be greater than the numbers with which you are working.
A **multiple** will always be equal to or greater than the numbers with which you are working.

Draw a line from the description on the left to the matching number set on the right.

1 Factors of 9   **A.** 6, 12, 18

2 Multiples of 9   **B.** 18

3 Factors of 6   **C.** 9, 18, 27

4 Multiples of 6   **D.** 1, 3, 9

5 Factors of 54   **E.** 18, 36, 54

6 GCF of 6 and 9   **F.** 3

7 LCM of 6 and 9   **G.** 1, 2, 3, 6

8 GCF of 54 and 9   **H.** 9

9 LCM of 54 and 6   **I.** 54

10 Common Multiples of 6 and 9   **J.** 1, 2, 3, 6, 9, 18, 27, 54

Name _____ Date _____

Prime and Composite Numbers

Prime: A natural number that has exactly two factors: the number itself and 1 (e.g., 2, 3, and 5).
Composite Number: A natural number that has three or more factors (e.g., 4, 6, 8, and 9).
   1 is neither prime nor composite.

Color blue each box with a multiple of the numbers 2 through 10, excluding the number itself (e.g., color 10, 15, 20, 25, but not the number 5). The remaining numbers should be prime numbers.

1	2	3	4	5	6	7	8	9	10
11	12	13	14	15	16	17	18	19	20
21	22	23	24	25	26	27	28	29	30
31	32	33	34	35	36	37	38	39	40
41	42	43	44	45	46	47	48	49	50
51	52	53	54	55	56	57	58	59	60
61	62	63	64	65	66	67	68	69	70
71	72	73	74	75	76	77	78	79	80
81	82	83	84	85	86	87	88	89	90
91	92	93	94	95	96	97	98	99	100

Pre-Algebra © 2004 Creative Teaching Press

Name _____ Date _____

Prime Factors of Natural Numbers

Prime Factorization: Expressing a number as a product of primes.

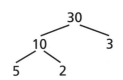

Therefore, 30 = 2 × 3 × 5.

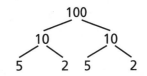

Therefore, 100 = 2 × 2 × 5 × 5.

Find the prime factorization or state that the number is prime.

1 66

2 325

3 23

4 451

5 494

6 29

7 If you have three prime numbers, then what would be the GCF? Explain your reasoning and give an example.

_____

_____

_____

_____

Using Prime Factors to Find the GCF

Find the GCF for the numbers 180, 594, and 2,574.

$180 = 2 \times 2 \times 3 \times 3 \times 5$

$594 = 2 \times 3 \times 3 \times 3 \times 5$

$2,574 = 2 \times 3 \times 3 \times 11 \times 13$

Common Factors: 2, 3, 3

The GCF: $2 \times 3 \times 3 = 18$

Use prime factorization to find the GCF for each set of numbers.

1 245 and 105

2 330, 495, and 825

_____

_____

3 792, 144, and 72

4 1,463 and 1,045

_____

_____

5 899 and 1,015

6 41, 67, and 97

_____

_____

Pre-Algebra © 2004 Creative Teaching Press

Prime Factors and the LCM

Find the LCM for the numbers 140 and 1,078.
$$140 = 2 \times 2 \times 7 \times 5$$
$$1,078 = 2 \times 7 \times 7 \times 11$$
$$2 \times 2 \times 7 \times 5$$
$$2 \times 7 \times 7 \times 11$$
Factors: 2, 2, 5, 7, 7, 11
LCM: $2 \times 2 \times 5 \times 7 \times 7 \times 11 = 10,780$

Use prime factorization to find the LCM for each set of numbers.

1 35, 245, and 105

_____

2 40, 210, and 165

_____

3 30, 99, and 425

_____

4 46, 69, and 115

_____

5 343, 125, and 1,225

_____

6 315, 561, and 5,049

_____

7 If you have three prime numbers, then what would be the LCM?
Explain your reasoning and give an example.

_____

_____

_____

Name _____ Date _____

Vocabulary Review

Review

Fill in the blank.

1 _____: a collection of objects.

2 Whole Numbers: The set of numbers _____.

3 Fractions: Part of a _____.

4 _____: A number with one or more digits to the right of the decimal.

5 _____: A single number. 0, 1, 2, 3, 4, 5, 6, 7, 8, and 9.

6 Natural Numbers: The set of numbers starting with the number _____.

7 Integers: The set of numbers _____.

8 _____: This is the set of all integers plus all of the terminating or repeating decimals between the whole numbers.

9 _____: This is the set of all numbers that are not rational.

10 Sum: The answer to a(n) _____ problem.

11 Difference: The answer to a(n) _____ problem.

12 Product: The answer to a(n) _____ problem.

13 Quotient: The answer to a(n) _____ problem.

14 _____: The quotient of two numbers is a whole number.

15 _____: Numbers that are multiplied or numbers that are divisible by a number.

16 _____: The product of a number and a whole number.

17 Prime: A natural number that only has two factors, _____ and _____.

18 _____: A number that is a factor of two or more numbers.

19 _____: The greatest factor of two or more numbers.

20 _____: A number that is a multiple of two or more numbers.

Pre-Algebra © 2004 Creative Teaching Press

Looking Back

REVIEW

Answer the question or provide the needed information. Show your work.

1 I am a natural number less than $1\frac{1}{2}$. What am I? _____

2 I am a natural number between ⁻1 and 2. What am I? _____

3 What integers between and including 2 and 10 is the number 1,260 evenly divisible by? _____

4 What integers between and including 2 and 10 is the number 720 evenly divisible by? _____

5 What is the GCF of 87 and 58? _____

6 What is the LCM of 36 and 72? _____

7 List two multiples of 10. _____ _____

8 List two factors of 10. _____ _____

9 Name one prime greater than 5. _____

10 Find the prime factorization of 330. _____

11 Use prime factorization to find the GCF of 525 and 693. _____

12 Use prime factorization to find the GCF of 420 and 252. _____

Terminating and Repeating Decimals

Decimals that are rational numbers are either **repeating** or **terminating** decimals.
- 0.5 and 0.25 are terminating decimals.
- 0.$\overline{3}$, 0.1$\overline{6}$, and 0.$\overline{142857}$ are repeating decimals with a pattern that never ends.

Write each fraction from the fraction box beneath the appropriate heading.

$\dfrac{1}{2}$	$\dfrac{1}{3}$	$\dfrac{1}{4}$	$\dfrac{1}{5}$	$\dfrac{1}{6}$	$\dfrac{1}{7}$	$\dfrac{1}{8}$	$\dfrac{1}{9}$	$\dfrac{1}{10}$	$\dfrac{2}{3}$	$\dfrac{3}{4}$	$\dfrac{2}{5}$
$\dfrac{5}{6}$	$\dfrac{2}{7}$	$\dfrac{5}{7}$	$\dfrac{3}{8}$	$\dfrac{2}{9}$	$\dfrac{7}{9}$	$\dfrac{3}{10}$	$\dfrac{3}{5}$	$\dfrac{6}{7}$	$\dfrac{5}{8}$	$\dfrac{4}{9}$	$\dfrac{8}{9}$

Terminating	Repeating

Fractions to Decimals

$$\frac{2}{3} = 2 \div 3 = 0.\overline{6}$$

Draw a line from the fraction on the left to the decimal of the same value on the right.

1 $\frac{2}{3}$

A. $0.8\overline{3}$

2 $\frac{5}{6}$

B. 0.83

3 $\frac{2}{9}$

C. 0.2

4 $\frac{83}{100}$

D. $0.2\overline{2}$

5 $\frac{1}{5}$

E. 0.416

6 $\frac{52}{125}$

F. $0.41\overline{6}$

7 $\frac{1}{11}$

G. 0.09

8 $\frac{9}{100}$

H. $0.0\overline{9}$

9 $\frac{2}{11}$

I. 0.18

10 $\frac{3}{5}$

J. $0.\overline{18}$

11 $\frac{9}{50}$

K. 0.6

12 $\frac{5}{12}$

L. $0.\overline{6}$

Pre-Algebra © 2004 Creative Teaching Press

Line It Up!

$$24.56 + 3.123 + 27.683 =$$

```
  24.56
   3.123
+ 27.683
  55.366
```

Solve.

1 231.7 + 4.56 = _____

2 5.244 – 0.921 = _____

3 4.05 + 3.98 = _____

4 6.7 – 0.12 = _____

5 0.0335 + 0.05 = _____

6 1 – 0.921 = _____

7 4.5 – 3.221 = _____

8 0.02 + 0.12 = _____

9 2.34 + 5.67 + 4.35 + 1.22 = _____

10 10 – 3.5 – 2.3 = _____

11 89.53 – 1.054 – 0.2 – 0.0087 = _____

12 1000 – 5.245 – 4.02 – 988.065 = _____

13 0.999 – 0.5555 + 0.22222 = _____

14 56.78 – 4.395 – 48.065 – 4.29 = _____

Pre-Algebra © 2004 Creative Teaching Press

Name _____ Date _____

Multiplying with Decimals

$24.56 \times 3.123 = 76.70088$

2   3   5 decimal places total

$0.00003 \times 0.0001 = 0.000000003$

5   4   9 decimal places total

Find the product.

1 $4.5 \times 10 =$ _____

2 $5.244 \times 0.921 =$ _____

3 $4.05 \times 3 =$ _____

4 $60 \times 0.12 =$ _____

5 $0.0335 \times 0.05 =$ _____

6 $10 \times 0.921 =$ _____

7 $5 \times 3.221 =$ _____

8 $0.02 \times 0.12 =$ _____

9 $12.4 \times 3.4 \times 2.7 =$ _____

10 $100 \times 0.001 =$ _____

11 $24.02 \times 33.2 \times 4.1 =$ _____

12 $1.1 \times 2.2 \times 3.3 \times 4.4 =$ _____

13 $10 \times 5.2 \times 100 \times 5.45 =$ _____

14 $100 \times 0.01 \times 1000 \times 0.02 \times 0.3 =$ _____

Dividing with Decimals

$$40 \div 0.02 = 0.02\overline{)40.00} = 2\overline{)4000}^{2000}$$

Solve.

1 $4.6 \div 2.3 =$ _____

2 $7.5 \div 0.25 =$ _____

3 $110 \div 1.1 =$ _____

4 $60 \div 0.12 =$ _____

5 $810 \div 0.09 =$ _____

6 $310.5 \div 4.5 =$ _____

7 $5 \div 2.5 =$ _____

8 $40.32 \div 1.6 =$ _____

9 $128.57544 \div 2.367 =$ _____

10 $100 \div 0.001 =$ _____

11 $150 \div 0.25 =$ _____

12 $56.2 \div 0.02 =$ _____

13 $66.0543 \div 0.001 =$ _____

14 $10000 \div 0.05 =$ _____

Pre-Algebra © 2004 Creative Teaching Press

Multiples of Ten

$345 \times 1{,}000 = 345{,}000$	$2.345 \times 100 = 234.5$
$345 \div 1{,}000 = 0.345$	$2.345 \div 100 = 0.02345$

Solve.

1 $789 \times 10 =$ _____

2 $654 \div 100 =$ _____

3 $5.67 \times 1{,}000 =$ _____

4 $56.43 \div 100 =$ _____

5 $5.47 \times 100{,}000 =$ _____

6 $0.001 \times 100 =$ _____

7 $1.99 \div 1{,}000 =$ _____

8 $0.34 \div 100 =$ _____

9 $245.876 \times 100 =$ _____

10 $789.2 \div 100 =$ _____

11 $576.98 \times 1{,}000 =$ _____

12 $763 \div 100 =$ _____

13 $908.005 \times 10{,}000 =$ _____

14 $765.4 \div 100 =$ _____

15 $0.001 \times 1{,}000 =$ _____

16 $22.22 \div 100 =$ _____

17 $5.05 \times 100 =$ _____

18 $879654.56 \div 1{,}000{,}000 =$ _____

19 $0.00007 \times 10{,}000{,}000 =$ _____

20 $3456.005 \div 100{,}000{,}000 =$ _____

Rounding

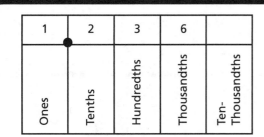

Round 1.236 to the nearest tenth.
1.236 ⟶ 1.2

Round 1.236 to the nearest hundredth.
1.236 ⟶ 1.24

Round each number to the indicated place value.

1 Round 12.3456 to the nearest tenth _____

2 Round 3.0345 to the nearest thousandth _____

3 Round 7.789 to the nearest hundredth _____

4 Round 2.15672 to the nearest ten-thousandth _____

5 Round 3.45499 to the nearest hundredth _____

6 Round 9.012 to the nearest tenth _____

7 Round 3.6743 to the nearest thousandth _____

8 Round 315.697243 to the nearest thousandth _____

9 Round 654.145419 to the nearest hundredth _____

10 Round 0.012 to the nearest tenth _____

11 Round 1.629543 to the nearest thousandth _____

12 Round 98.9542 to the nearest tenth _____

13 Round 6.00003 to the nearest ten-thousandth _____

14 Round 3.9999 to the nearest thousandth _____

Pre-Algebra © 2004 Creative Teaching Press

Mix It Up!

Draw a line to match the underlined digit on the left with the corresponding place value on the right.

1 1.23<u>4</u>5   **A.** Tenths

2 <u>1</u>.2345   **B.** Ten-Thousandths

3 1.234<u>5</u>   **C.** Ones

4 1.2<u>3</u>45   **D.** Hundredths

5 1.<u>2</u>345   **E.** Thousandths

Round each decimal to the named place value.

6 6.754 to the tenth

_____

7 9.5432 to the hundredth

_____

8 3.624834 to the ten-thousandth

_____

9 2.4596 to the thousandth

_____

Solve.

10 $345.6 - 3.221 =$ _____

11 $763.4 \div 100 =$ _____

12 $67.1 \times 0.023 =$ _____

13 $3.7417 \div 3.1 =$ _____

14 $5.4 \div 2 =$ _____

15 $1.5 \times 3.5 =$ _____

16 $567.0321 \times 10,000 =$ _____

17 $20.5 \div 2.5 =$ _____

18 $80.64 \div 1.6 =$ _____

19 $754.009 \times 100 =$ _____

20 $567.4 \div 100 =$ _____

21 $654.54 \div 100 \times 10 =$ _____

Name _____   Date _____

Understanding Rational Numbers

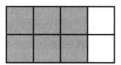

The shaded part of this rectangle is equal to $\frac{3}{4}$.

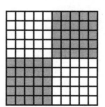

The shaded part of this grid is equal to 0.50.

Represent each rational number.

1 Shade the grid to represent 0.65.

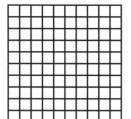

2 Shade the fraction strip to represent $\frac{1}{3}$.

3 Shade $\frac{1}{4}$ of an hour on the clock.

4 Shade the grid to represent 0.3.

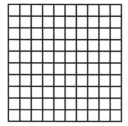

5 Shade the fraction strip to represent $\frac{1}{2}$.

6 Shade $\frac{1}{5}$ of an hour on the clock.

7 Shade the grid to represent 0.03.

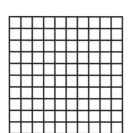

8 Shade the fraction strip to represent $\frac{1}{4}$.

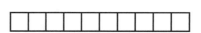

9 Shade $\frac{1}{10}$ of an hour on the clock.

Name _____ Date _____

Number Representations

If $\frac{1}{2}$ = ⬤ ; then 1 = ?

Draw a model to answer each question.

1 Represent $3\frac{1}{3}$ using the bars.

2 If $\frac{3}{4}$ = ⊕ ; then 1 = ?

3 If $\frac{4}{5}$ = △ ; then 1 = ?

4 If $1\frac{1}{2}$ = ▭ ; then 1 = ?

5 In $1\frac{1}{2}$ = ⊕ there are two equal shaded sections of the circle. What is each section equal to here?

6 If $1\frac{1}{2}$ = ⬤ ; then 1 = ?

7 Use a visual representation of your choice and words to explain how 0.6 is equal to $\frac{3}{5}$.

_____

Comparing Fractions

Denominator: The number of equal sections of the whole. Also, the bottom number of the fraction.

Numerator: The number of equal sections that the fraction represents. Also, the top number of the fraction.

$$\frac{1}{3} \qquad \frac{1}{8}$$

$$\frac{8}{24} \qquad\qquad \frac{3}{24}$$

$$\frac{1}{3} > \frac{1}{8}$$

Compare the fractions. Write the symbol that makes the statement correct.

1 $\frac{1}{8} \bigcirc \frac{1}{5}$

2 $\frac{2}{3} \bigcirc \frac{3}{5}$

3 $\frac{1}{4} \bigcirc \frac{1}{5}$

4 $\frac{2}{4} \bigcirc \frac{1}{2}$

5 $\frac{8}{9} \bigcirc \frac{9}{8}$

6 $\frac{1}{6} \bigcirc \frac{4}{25}$

7 $\frac{1}{7} \bigcirc \frac{71}{500}$

8 $\frac{3}{25} \bigcirc \frac{1}{8}$

9 $\frac{1}{5} \bigcirc \frac{5}{25}$

10 $\frac{6}{7} \bigcirc \frac{428,571}{500,000}$

Pre-Algebra © 2004 Creative Teaching Press

Comparing Small and Large Decimals

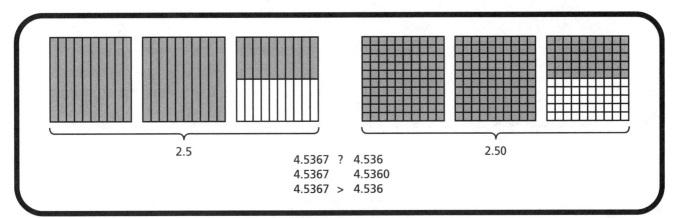

2.5   2.50

4.5367 ? 4.536
4.5367   4.5360
4.5367 > 4.536

Compare the decimals. Write the symbol that makes the statement correct.

1 67.78 ◯ 67.87

2 5.643 ◯ 3.643

3 3.445 ◯ 3.4

4 5.50 ◯ 5.500

5 100.1 ◯ 100.01

6 6.53 ◯ 6.6

7 0.0001 ◯ 0.00001

8 2.3 ◯ 2.03

9 0.987 ◯ 1.23

10 0.0899 ◯ 0.00989

11 0.0234 + 0.4567 ◯ 0.0234 × 0.4567

12 0.945 − 0.5 ◯ 0.945 ÷ 0.5

Number Lines

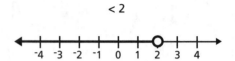

Represent the following values.

1 ≥ 4

-6 -5 -4 -3 -2 -1 0 1 2 3 4 5 6

2 < 5

-6 -5 -4 -3 -2 -1 0 1 2 3 4 5 6

3 ≥ ⁻3

-6 -5 -4 -3 -2 -1 0 1 2 3 4 5 6

4 ≤ 0

-6 -5 -4 -3 -2 -1 0 1 2 3 4 5 6

5 > 2.5

-6 -5 -4 -3 -2 -1 0 1 2 3 4 5 6

6 ≤ $3\frac{3}{4}$

-6 -5 -4 -3 -2 -1 0 1 2 3 4 5 6

7 ≤ 5 and > 2

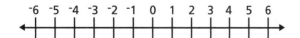

8 < 2 and ≥ 5

Pre-Algebra © 2004 Creative Teaching Press

Negative Numbers: + and –

Negative Numbers: Numbers less than zero.

Addition
Pos + Pos = Pos
Pos + Neg = Greater Sign
Neg + Pos = Greater Sign
Neg + Neg = Neg

Subtraction
5 – 6 becomes 5 + (⁻6) = ⁻1
⁻5 – (⁻6) becomes ⁻5 + 6 = 1

Solve.

1 ⁻3 + (⁻2) = _____

2 ⁻3 – (⁻2) = _____

3 ⁻4 + (⁻5) = _____

4 ⁻10 – (⁻5) = _____

5 ⁻4 – 6 = _____

6 12 – (⁻12) = _____

7 15 + (⁻29) = _____

8 ⁻7 – 7 = _____

9 8 + (⁻6) = _____

10 ⁻20 – (⁻4) = _____

11 ⁻25 – 55 = _____

12 60 + (⁻10) = _____

Negative Numbers: × and ÷

Multiplication	Division
Pos x Pos = Pos	Pos ÷ Pos = Pos
Pos x Neg = Neg	Pos ÷ Neg = Neg
Neg x Neg = Pos	Neg ÷ Neg = Pos

Solve.

1 5 × (⁻9) = _____

2 ⁻7 × (⁻7) = _____

3 ⁻100 ÷ (⁻2) = _____

4 ⁻1 ÷ (⁻2) = _____

5 ⁻4 × 5 = _____

6 ⁻10 ÷ 5 = _____

7 ⁻4 × 6 = _____

8 12 ÷ (⁻12) = _____

9 ⁻8 × (⁻6) = _____

10 ⁻20 ÷ (⁻4) = _____

11 ⁻5 × 5 × (⁻10) = _____

12 6 × (⁻10) × (⁻2) × (⁻1) = _____

Watch Out!

Solve.

1 345 − (⁻3) = _____

2 ⁻763 ÷ (⁻100) = _____

3 ⁻6 × 2 = _____

4 ⁻897 + (⁻31) = _____

5 5.4 ÷ (⁻2) = _____

6 ⁻1.5 × (⁻3.5) = _____

7 ⁻361.0321 × 10,000 = _____

8 20.5 ÷ 2.5 = _____

9 80.64 ÷ (⁻1.6) = _____

10 ⁻754.009 × 100 = _____

11 ⁻567.4 ÷ (⁻100) = _____

12 654.54 ÷ (⁻100) × 10 = _____

Finding Absolute Value

Absolute Value: The distance to a number from zero. It is denoted $|x|$ and is read "the absolute value of x."

$$|{}^-4| = 4 \text{ and } |4| = 4$$

Simplify.

1 $|{}^-4| =$ _____

2 $|5| =$ _____

3 $|8 - 4| =$ _____

4 $|4 - 8| =$ _____

5 ${}^-|7| =$ _____

6 ${}^-|{}^-7| =$ _____

7 ${}^-|{}^-3| + |{}^-3| =$ _____

8 $|{}^-8| - |{}^-4| =$ _____

9 $|{}^-6| \cdot |{}^-4| =$ _____

10 $|{}^-2| \cdot |{}^-8| =$ _____

11 $|{}^-4 \cdot 5| =$ _____

12 $|{}^-4 \div {}^-2| =$ _____

13 ${}^-({}^-|{}^-10|) =$ _____

14 $|{}^-5| + |{}^-7 \cdot 3| =$ _____

15 ${}^-|{}^-4| + |{}^-5 \cdot 2| =$ _____

16 ${}^-|{}^-8| + {}^-(|{}^-9 \cdot 4|) =$ _____

17 ${}^-|{}^-9| - {}^-(|{}^-10 \cdot 7|) =$ _____

18 ${}^-|{}^-4| \cdot {}^-(|{}^-3 \cdot 2|) =$ _____

Pre-Algebra © 2004 Creative Teaching Press

Adding and Subtracting Like Fractions

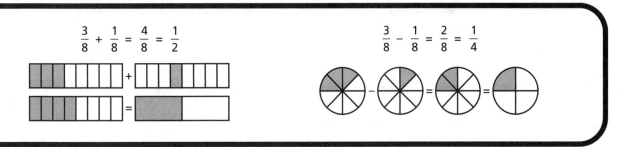

$$\frac{3}{8} + \frac{1}{8} = \frac{4}{8} = \frac{1}{2} \qquad\qquad \frac{3}{8} - \frac{1}{8} = \frac{2}{8} = \frac{1}{4}$$

Solve. Write the answer in lowest terms. Show your work with an illustrated model.

1 $\dfrac{3}{8} - \dfrac{2}{8} =$

2 $\dfrac{7}{10} + \dfrac{8}{10} =$

3 $\dfrac{5}{6} - \dfrac{4}{6} =$

4 $\dfrac{7}{8} - \dfrac{4}{8} =$

5 $\dfrac{1}{3} + \dfrac{2}{3} =$

6 $\dfrac{3}{5} + \dfrac{4}{5} =$

7 $\dfrac{5}{9} - \dfrac{2}{9} =$

8 $\dfrac{3}{12} + \dfrac{5}{12} =$

9 $\dfrac{13}{36} + \dfrac{5}{36} =$

Adding and Subtracting Unlike Fractions

$$\frac{1}{4} + \frac{3}{8} = \frac{2}{8} + \frac{3}{8} = \frac{5}{8} \qquad\qquad \frac{5}{12} - \frac{3}{8} = \frac{10}{24} - \frac{9}{24} = \frac{1}{24}$$

Rewrite the fractions in like terms. Solve. Simplify if needed.

1 $\frac{3}{8} + \frac{2}{3} =$

2 $\frac{7}{8} - \frac{8}{10} =$

3 $\frac{1}{5} - \frac{1}{6} =$

4 $\frac{1}{8} + \frac{1}{3} =$

5 $\frac{1}{3} + \frac{2}{5} =$

6 $\frac{1}{4} + \frac{4}{5} =$

7 $\frac{5}{8} - \frac{1}{3} =$

8 $\frac{2}{7} - \frac{2}{9} =$

9 $\frac{9}{14} + \frac{6}{28} =$

10 $\frac{11}{18} + \frac{5}{54} =$

11 $\frac{5}{7} - \frac{3}{5} =$

12 $\frac{31}{72} - \frac{3}{8} =$

13 $\frac{7}{6} + \frac{2}{3} =$

14 $\frac{2}{3} - \frac{8}{27} =$

15 $\frac{13}{16} - \frac{1}{8} =$

Pre-Algebra © 2004 Creative Teaching Press

Multiplying Fractions

$$\frac{1}{3} \times \frac{2}{7} = \frac{2}{21}$$

Solve.

1 $\dfrac{2}{3} \times \dfrac{1}{3} =$

2 $\dfrac{1}{4} \times \dfrac{1}{3} =$

3 $\dfrac{1}{8} \times 8 =$

4 $\dfrac{2}{5} \times \dfrac{1}{2} =$

5 $\dfrac{1}{4} \times \dfrac{1}{2} =$

6 $\dfrac{1}{7} \times \dfrac{1}{4} =$

7 $1 \times \dfrac{1}{3} =$

8 $\dfrac{1}{10} \times 2 =$

9 $\dfrac{8}{9} \times \dfrac{25}{27} =$

10 $1\dfrac{1}{4} \times 1\dfrac{1}{3} =$

11 $5\dfrac{1}{2} \times 2 =$

12 $2\dfrac{1}{4} \times 3\dfrac{1}{3} =$

13 $\dfrac{3}{4} \times \dfrac{1}{8} \times \dfrac{7}{8} =$

14 $4\dfrac{1}{2} \times 1\dfrac{5}{8} \times 2\dfrac{1}{3} =$

Finding Reciprocals

Fraction	Reciprocal
$\dfrac{3}{4}$	$\dfrac{4}{3}$
$\dfrac{8}{3}$	$\dfrac{3}{8}$

Write the reciprocal of the number and then multiply to prove the product is equal to 1.

1 $\dfrac{1}{3}$

2 $\dfrac{2}{3}$

3 $\dfrac{1}{8}$

4 $\dfrac{5}{6}$

5 $\dfrac{2}{7}$

6 $\dfrac{4}{9}$

7 $\dfrac{9}{8}$

8 $\dfrac{9}{11}$

9 6

10 1

11 100

12 $-\dfrac{2}{3}$

13 $-\dfrac{9}{8}$

14 $-\dfrac{10}{11}$

15 $^-5$

16 0

Dividing with Fractions

$$\frac{1}{2} \div \frac{1}{4} = \frac{1}{2} \times \frac{4}{1} = \frac{4}{2} = 2$$

Find the quotient.

1 $\dfrac{1}{4} \div \dfrac{1}{8} =$

2 $\dfrac{3}{8} \div \dfrac{1}{4} =$

3 $\dfrac{5}{6} \div \dfrac{1}{3} =$

4 $5 \div \dfrac{1}{5} =$

5 $\dfrac{1}{4} \div 5 =$

6 $^-6 \div \dfrac{1}{3} =$

7 $-\dfrac{4}{5} \div -\dfrac{1}{4} =$

8 $\dfrac{1}{10} \div {}^-10 =$

9 $\dfrac{1}{7} \div \dfrac{4}{5} =$

10 $-\dfrac{1}{2} \div \dfrac{1}{8} =$

11 $-\dfrac{5}{24} \div 5 =$

12 $-\dfrac{1}{3} \div \dfrac{1}{3} =$

13 $-\dfrac{1}{9} \div -\dfrac{8}{9} =$

14 $\dfrac{1}{10} \div {}^-1{,}000 =$

15 $\dfrac{3}{10} \div \dfrac{2}{9} =$

16 $\dfrac{8}{9} \div \dfrac{2}{7} =$

Mental Models of Dividing Fractions

$\frac{1}{2} \div \frac{1}{4}$

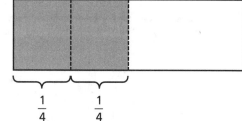

$\frac{1}{4}$ $\frac{1}{4}$

$\frac{1}{2}$ divided into quarters is two quarters of the whole.

$\frac{1}{2} \div \frac{1}{3}$

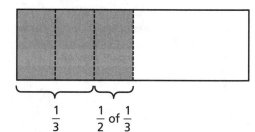

$\frac{1}{3}$ $\frac{1}{2}$ of $\frac{1}{3}$

$\frac{1}{2}$ divided into thirds is one and one-half third of the whole.

Solve. Then represent each problem with an illustrated model like the ones in the example box.

1 $\frac{3}{4} \div \frac{1}{4} =$

2 $\frac{7}{8} \div \frac{1}{4} =$

3 $3 \div \frac{1}{5} =$

4 $4\frac{1}{2} \div \frac{1}{8} =$

Pre-Algebra © 2004 Creative Teaching Press

Ordering Decimals

order: 2.3, 1.45, 1.4, 2.5, 2, 1.54

1.4
1.45
1.54
2
2.3
2.5

Put each set of numbers in **increasing** order.

1 0, ⁻3, ⁻2.2, ⁻2.5, ⁻1, ⁻0.5

2 3.3, 3.35, 3.4, 3.45, 3.43

3 ⁻0.5, ⁻0.55, ⁻0.65, ⁻0.45, ⁻1.1, ⁻0.05, ⁻0.01

Put each set of numbers in **decreasing** order.

4 3.1, 3.0, 3.35, 4.5, 2.6, 2.2

5 1, ⁻1.5, ⁻1.6, 2, 2.3, 2.8, ⁻5

6 1.15, ⁻1.5, 0, ⁻0.7, 0.8, 0.5, ⁻1.3

Percents

$$34\% = 0.34 = \frac{34}{100} = \frac{17}{50}$$

Complete the chart.

	Percent	Decimal	Fraction
1	45%		
2	210%		
3	0.4%		
4		0.123	
5			$\frac{3}{10}$
6			$\frac{1}{3}$
7		0.125	
8	1%		
9			$\frac{1}{11}$
10	14%		
11			$\frac{7}{8}$
12			$\frac{2}{3}$
13		$0.1\overline{6}$	
14		0.25	

Name _____ Date _____

Percent Perfection

Review

Determine the shaded percent of each figure.

 _____

 _____

 _____

 _____

Draw a representation of each percent.

5 25%

6 125%

7 2%

Answer the following questions.

8 The sugar jar has 4 cups of sugar when full. Johnny ate 1% of the sugar in the jar. Explain what this means in your own words. Is this possible? Why or why not?

9 On a recent test, Randy only got 2 questions correct out of 10. The teacher let him retake it and he got 350% more correct. Explain what this means in your own words. Is this possible? Why or why not?

10 A cell phone commercial stated that 110% of your calls will be cheaper with their company. Explain what this means in your own words. Is this possible? Why or why not?

11 Maggie read 0.1% of the books at her school library. Explain what this means in your own words. Is this possible? Why or why not?

Ordering Decimals, Percents, and Fractions

Review

Order the data sets in increasing order. Show all work.

1 5, 5.5, 560%, $5\frac{1}{4}$

2 ⁻4, ⁻$4\frac{1}{2}$, 4, 0, 435%

3 $\frac{1}{4}$, $\frac{1}{2}$, 35%, 0.4

4 $1\frac{1}{8}$, 0.2, 25%, ⁻2, $\frac{2}{3}$

5 ⁻$2\frac{1}{2}$, ⁻$2\frac{3}{4}$, ⁻2.55, ⁻2.45, ⁻4.8

6 61%, 0.7, $\frac{2}{3}$, $\frac{3}{4}$

Money

Visual Model	Dollars	Cents
(dollar bill, dime, dime, penny)	$1.31	131¢
(quarter, quarter, dime, penny)	$0.61	61¢

Complete the chart.

	Visual Model	Dollars	Cents
1	(nickel, dime, dime, penny)		
2		$2.50	
3			99¢
4	(dollar bill, quarter, quarter, quarter) (dollar bill, dime, dime, dime)		
5			500¢
6		$1.99	

Cents and Dollars

Read the sign. Answer the questions.

1 What kind of coin could pay for the soft drink?

2 What is the difference between 99¢ and 0.99¢?

3 Pretend that you are explaining to the store manager what is wrong with the sign. What would you say?

4 Name a situation where you might actually use a decimal with a ¢ sign.

Pre-Algebra © 2004 Creative Teaching Press

Discounts

A $35 sweater is on sale for 30% off.
How much is the discount?   30% = 0.30 $35 × 0.30 = $10.50 discount
How much is the new price?   100% − 30% = 70% $35 × 0.70 = $24.50 sale price

Solve.

1 A store offers 40% off its merchandise. What is the discount on a $68 outfit?

2 A store offers 25% off its merchandise. What is the sale price of a $75 outfit?

3 A store offers 15% off its merchandise. What is the discount on a $36 pair of jeans?

4 A store offers 10% off its merchandise. What is the sale price of a $28 shirt?

5 A store offers 30% off its merchandise. What is the discount on a $20 game?

6 A store offers 25% off its merchandise. What is the sale price of a $50 pair of shoes?

7 A store offers 5% off its merchandise. What is the discount on a $40 watch?

8 A store offers 20% off its merchandise. What is the sale price of a $35 shirt?

9 A store offers 15% off its merchandise. What is the discount on a $1,049 pair of earrings?

10 A store offers 25% off merchandise that is already discounted by 30%. Is this **the same as** a 55% discount off the original price? Write an example to illustrate your reasoning.

Name _____ Date _____

Working with Coins

Determine the value of each coin based on the clues in the squares.

Coin A + Coin B + Coin C + Coin D = 41¢

Coin B + Coin A + Coin A + Coin B = 52¢

Coin C + Coin D + Coin D + Coin D = 35¢

Coin D + Coin B + Coin A + Coin B = 37¢

Coin A =   Coin B =

Coin C =   Coin D =

Pre-Algebra © 2004 Creative Teaching Press

Rational Numbers

Review

Use the clues to complete the puzzle.

Across

1. _____: The bottom number of the fraction.
2. _____: The top number of the fraction.
6. _____: A way of expressing hundredths.
7. _____: Distance from zero.

Down

1. The symbol $ will always refer to amounts in terms of _____.
3. The product of two _____ is 1.
4. The symbol ¢ will always refer to amounts in terms of _____.
5. _____: Decimals that follow a pattern.

Vocabulary Scramble

R E V I E W

Unscramble each word. Copy the letters from the numbered boxes to the corresponding cells below to figure out the message.

1 NIAREGTEP LADSECIM

⬜⬜⬜⬜⬜⬜⬜⬜ ⬜⬜⬜⬜⬜⬜⬜
22 10 14   38   5

2 NERGNTAMTII DALCESIM

⬜⬜⬜⬜⬜⬜⬜⬜⬜⬜ ⬜⬜⬜⬜⬜⬜⬜
37   2   12

3 TODNONRAEMI

⬜⬜⬜⬜⬜⬜⬜⬜⬜⬜⬜
6 17   27   25   15

4 NAUTEORMR

⬜⬜⬜⬜⬜⬜⬜⬜⬜
33   24 1 18   30

5 SESL NATH

⬜⬜⬜⬜ ⬜⬜⬜⬜
34   39   20   9

6 RETAGRE TANH

⬜⬜⬜⬜⬜⬜⬜ ⬜⬜⬜⬜
4   23

7 LESBAOTU LUVEA

⬜⬜⬜⬜⬜⬜⬜⬜ ⬜⬜⬜⬜⬜
26   13   3   28 35

8 RECPILRACO

⬜⬜⬜⬜⬜⬜⬜⬜⬜⬜
7 31 8   16 21 19 32

9 PEERCTN

⬜⬜⬜⬜⬜⬜
36   29   11

W								F							F					
1	2	3	4	5	6	7	8	9	10	11	12	13	14		15	16	17	18	19	20

	F																			Y		W			
21		22	23	24	25	26	27	28	29	28	30	31	32	26	33	34	35	36				27	37	38	39

58

Name _____ Date _____

Rational Review 1

Solve the expressions.

1 3.789 + 123.567 = _____

2 ⁻2 − 6 = _____

3 6 × (⁻3) = _____

4 ⁻48 ÷ (⁻8) = _____

5 $\dfrac{1}{2} + \dfrac{1}{3} =$ _____

6 $\dfrac{1}{4} \div \dfrac{2}{3} =$ _____

7 $\dfrac{7}{8} \times \dfrac{3}{5} =$ _____

8 $-\dfrac{3}{5} \div \dfrac{1}{2} =$ _____

9 Write the fractions and decimals in order from least to greatest.

0.15, $\dfrac{1}{9}$, $\dfrac{1}{3}$, 0.2, 0.3

10 Write the fractions in order from least to greatest.

$\dfrac{1}{2}, \dfrac{1}{4}, \dfrac{1}{5}, \dfrac{1}{6}, \dfrac{1}{7}$

11 Shade the graph to represent $\dfrac{7}{10}$.

12 If $\dfrac{2}{3} =$ ⬤ , then 1 =

13 Write the symbol that makes the statement true:

$\dfrac{2}{3}$ ◯ $\dfrac{1}{2}$

14 Write the symbol that makes the statement true:

1.52 ◯ 1.5

15 What inverse would you use to solve for **a** in the equation a ÷ 3 = 2?

16 What is the decimal equivalent of 0.7%?

17 What is the fraction equivalent of 145%?

18 What is the shaded portion of the figure?

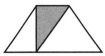

19 Rewrite the monetary amount 55¢ using a $ sign.

20 What is the reciprocal of $\dfrac{5}{6}$?

Pre-Algebra © 2004 Creative Teaching Press

Name _____ Date _____

Rational Review 2

Solve the expressions.

1 790.2345 − 7.9 = _____

2 ⁻5 + 11 = _____

3 ⁻3 × (⁻4) = _____

4 ⁻36 ÷ 6 = _____

5 $\dfrac{1}{3} - \dfrac{1}{5}$ = _____

6 $-\dfrac{2}{5} \div \left(-\dfrac{3}{8}\right)$ = _____

7 $-\dfrac{1}{5} \times \dfrac{5}{8}$ = _____

8 $-\dfrac{3}{5} \div \left(-\dfrac{1}{3}\right)$ = _____

9 Write the fractions and decimals in order from least to greatest.

$0.1, \ \dfrac{1}{8}, \ \dfrac{1}{11}, \ 0.2, \ 0.13$

10 Write the fractions in order from least to greatest.

$\dfrac{1}{3}, \ \dfrac{1}{4}, \ \dfrac{1}{8}, \ \dfrac{1}{6}, \ \dfrac{1}{9}$

11 Shade the bar below to represent $\dfrac{30}{100}$.

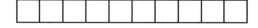

12 If $\dfrac{1}{2}$ = , then $1\dfrac{1}{2}$ =

13 Write the symbol that makes the statement true:

$\dfrac{1}{5} \bigcirc \dfrac{2}{11}$

14 Write the symbol that makes the statement true:

3.700 $\bigcirc$ 3.7

15 What inverse would you use to solve for **a** in the equation **a** × 5 = 4?

16 What is the decimal equivalent of 20.5%?

17 What is the fraction equivalent of 300%?

18 What is the shaded percent of the figure?

19 Rewrite the monetary amount $0.99 using a ¢ sign.

20 What is the reciprocal of $\dfrac{1}{3}$?

Pre-Algebra © 2004 Creative Teaching Press

Ratios and Rates

Ratio: Represents the relationship of two quantities that have the same units of measure. Ratios can be written:

$$\frac{1}{3}, \text{ 1 to 3, or 1:3}$$

Box Height = 20 inches Box Width = 10 inches

$$\frac{20}{10} = \frac{2}{1} \text{ or 2 to 1}$$

Rate: Represents the relationship of two quantities that have different units of measure.

Trip Distance = 250 miles Trip Time = 5 hours

$$\frac{250}{5} = \frac{50}{1} \text{ or 50 miles per hour}$$

State whether the relationship is a ratio or a rate. Simplify.

1 $\dfrac{80 \text{ pieces of candy}}{20 \text{ students}} =$

2 $\dfrac{100 \text{ points}}{5 \text{ players}} =$

3 $\dfrac{90 \text{ doctors}}{80 \text{ doctors}} =$

4 $\dfrac{35 \text{ seconds}}{1 \text{ minute}} =$

5 $\dfrac{48 \text{ seeds}}{6 \text{ pots}} =$

6 $\dfrac{50 \text{ beads}}{5 \text{ beads}} =$

7 $\dfrac{500 \text{ stars}}{10 \text{ flags}} =$

8 $\dfrac{400 \text{ minutes}}{10 \text{ hours}} =$

9 $\dfrac{60 \text{ pencils}}{12 \text{ students}} =$

Rewrite as a ratio or a rate.

10 The school has 5 teachers for every 100 students.

11 1 out of every 3 baskets was scored by Jimmy.

12 2 inches of every foot of wood is wasted by the builder.

Company Comparisons

To compare rates, look at each in its simplest form. Use the information to fill in the chart. Then determine the rates based on the cost per minute.

Company A
Clear As It Gets Plan:
Every call is $0.20 for each minute.

Company B
Connect And Talk Plan:
Every call is $0.35 to connect plus $0.15 for each minute.

Company C
It's Not Cheaper By The Dozen Plan: Every call is $0.25 for each of the first 12 minutes and only $0.10 for each additional minute.

Company D
Hope You Get To Talk Plan: Every call is $5.00 no matter how long the call.

1 Before you complete the chart, predict which company you think you would use.

Explain why. _____

	Company A	Company B	Company C	Company D
Cost for a 1-minute call:				
Rate for a 1-minute call:				
Cost for a 5-minute call:				
Rate for a 5-minute call:				
Cost for a 10-minute call:				
Rate for a 10-minute call:				
Cost for a 30-minute call:				
Rate for a 30-minute call:				
Cost for a 1-hour call:				
Rate for a 1-hour call:				
Cost for a 100-minute call:				
Rate for a 100-minute call:				

2 Review the company you chose in the prediction. Has your preferred company changed?

Why or why not? _____

Name _____ Date _____

Comparing Rates

Use the chart you made in Company Comparisons (page 62) to answer the following questions.

What company has the best rate for a . . .

1 1-minute call? _____   **2** 5-minute call? _____

3 10-minute call? _____   **4** 30-minute call? _____

5 60-minute call? _____   **6** 100-minute call? _____

For each company, list the pros and cons. (You may list situations.)

	PROS	CONS
Company A		
Company B		
Company C		
Company D		

Name _____ Date _____

Using Powers and Square Roots

Power: An expression that has a base and an exponent. The **base** is a factor that is multiplied by itself the number of times named by the **exponent**.

base 5 ^{3} exponent

Square Number: The product of a number and itself. Also, a number with the exponent of two.

Square Root: One of two equal factors of a number.

$$5^3 = 5 \times 5 \times 5 = 125$$
$$5^2 = 5 \times 5 = 25$$
$$\sqrt{25} = 5 \text{ or } ^-5$$
$$100^0 = 1, 5^0 = 1$$

The $\sqrt{2}$ is an irrational number. Square and square root are inverse operations!

Write the value of each expression.

1 1^{10} = _____

2 4^3 = _____

3 $\sqrt{9}$ = _____

4 2^4 = _____

5 3^1 = _____

6 $\sqrt{16}$ = _____

7 $\sqrt{81}$ = _____

8 $\sqrt{36}$ = _____

Write each expression in words.

9 6^7 _____

10 $\sqrt{16}$ _____

11 3^2 _____

Pre-Algebra © 2004 Creative Teaching Press

Value Chart

Fill in the chart to show the squared values and square roots.

x	x^2	$\sqrt{x^2}$
1		
2		
3		
4		
5		
6		
7		
8		
9		
10		

Order of Operations

Order of Operations: A mathematical procedure to evaluate an expression involving more than one mathematical operation.

The Order of Operations
1. First, evaluate any operations in PARENTHESES or brackets.
2. Second, evaluate any EXPONENTS.
3. Third, evaluate any MULTIPLICATION and DIVISION in order from left to right. If both operations are in an equation, evaluate whichever comes first from left to right.
4. Finally, evaluate any ADDITION and SUBTRACTION in order from left to right.

Evaluate the following expressions.

1 $[(6 + 7) + 3^2] \times (4 \div 8) =$ _____

2 $(2 + 3)^2 + (3 + 1)^2 =$ _____

3 $9 + 6 \div 3 \times 6 =$ _____

4 $7 + 14 - 3 + 5 \times 2^3 =$ _____

5 $11 + 3^2 - 4 \times (80 \div 10) =$ _____

6 $3^2 + 4 \times 3 \div 6 =$ _____

7 $[4 \times (5 + 6)] \div (4^2 - 12) =$ _____

8 $[(5 + 6) \times (9 - 2)] \div (2^4 - 5) =$ _____

9 $[4 + 7 \times (^-1 + 10)] - [^-3^2 - (^-8)] =$ _____

10 $[(^-10 \div 2) \times (^-8 - 3)] - (2^2 \times 2) =$ _____

11 $^-1 \times [^-4 \times (5 + 6)] \div (^-1) \times (5^0) =$ _____

12 $(5^3) \times (9 - 2) \div (2^4 \div 2^2) =$ _____

Pre-Algebra © 2004 Creative Teaching Press

Take the Challenge

Fill in the blank with a number that will make the expression correct.

1 $8 + \underline{\hspace{1cm}} \div 4 = 12$

2 $6 + \underline{\hspace{1cm}}^2 \div 3 = 9$

3 $2 \times \underline{\hspace{1cm}} + 5 - (1 \times 2) = 11$

4 $9 + 6 \div \underline{\hspace{1cm}} \times 6 = 21$

5 $7 + 14 - 3 + 5 \times 2 \times \underline{\hspace{1cm}} = 58$

6 $\underline{\hspace{1cm}}^2 + 4 \times 3 \div 6 = 18$

Insert parentheses where necessary to make the expression true.

7 $7 + 3 \div 5 \times 2 + 3 = 7$

8 $7 + 3 \div 5 \times 2 + 3 = 10$

9 $7 + 3 \div 5 \times 2 + 3 = 11.2$

10 $2 + 3^2 + 3 + 1^2 = 41$

11 $2 + 3^2 + 3 + 1^2 = 15$

12 $2 + 3^2 + 3 + 1^2 = 27$

Evaluate each expression and state if it is *true* or *false*. If it is false, state the correct answer.

13 $6 + (4 - 2) \times 3^2 \div 6 = 7$

14 $6^2 + (3 - 1)^2 \times 3 \div 8 = 6$

15 $[(9 + 7) \div 2] - 3 = 5$

16 $(10 \times [(8 + 6) - (5 + 5)] \div 2)^2 = 10$

Estimating

Estimate: Calculate an amount close to the actual amount.

Decide if the expression is true or false. Then write a statement to support your answer.

1 $\frac{5}{6} = 1.2$

_____

2 $\frac{1}{3} = 0.5$

_____

3 $\frac{3}{4} + \frac{1}{3} = \frac{9}{10}$

_____

4 $\frac{1}{6} + \frac{1}{5} > \frac{1}{2}$

_____

5 $\frac{4}{5} + \frac{1}{4} \geq 1$

_____

6 $\frac{5}{6} + \frac{1}{5} > 1$

_____

7 $\frac{1}{2} + \frac{1}{3} + \frac{1}{6} \leq 1$

_____

8 $\frac{1}{9} + \frac{1}{4} < \frac{1}{2}$

_____

9 You have $6.00 and you purchase a drink for $3.10 and a bag of popcorn for $2.75.

_____

10 The original price of a T-shirt is $10. The sign above the rack states the shirts are 30% off. The shirt rings up for $8.50.

_____

Pre-Algebra © 2004 Creative Teaching Press

Mental Math

Use mental math to solve or estimate a solution for the problem. Attempt an exact solution first. Write *actual* or *estimate* after each answer.

1 Emily wants to buy 25 gum balls. They are 5/$1. _____

2 A package of ground beef is labeled 1.16 pounds.
The sign above the meat states the price is $3.20/pound. _____

3 Donuts are $4.00 per dozen. We want to buy 18 donuts. _____

4 You buy some bulk candy that is $2.80/pound. Your bag weighs 1.25 pounds.

_____

5 Sam needs to fill his gas tank with 15 gallons of gas. The gas is $1.54/gallon.

_____

Explain why an estimated answer is appropriate.

6 Kristina has a party in 3.5 hours. She estimates that it will take her 1 hour to prepare the food, 1 hour to decorate, and 30 minutes to get herself ready. She is trying to figure out if she has enough time to take a shower first.

_____

_____

7 Michael has $90. He wants to buy 1 video game and 2 memory cards. Without shopping, he estimates that a video should be less than $50 and each memory card should be $10 to $15. He is trying to figure out if he needs more money before going to the store.

_____

_____

Understanding Large Numbers

Scientific Notation: A short form of writing numbers where the number is written as $n \times 10^x$ where **n** is a rational number from 1 to 9.

Rational	Scientific Notation
5,600	5.6×10^3
3,000,000	3×10^6
7,630,000,000	7.63×10^9

Express each number in scientific notation.

1 5,430,000 _____

2 210,000,000 _____

3 999,000 _____

4 6,780,000,000 _____

Express each scientific notation as a number.

5 3.45×10^8 _____

6 7×10^{10} _____

7 543.2×10^7 _____

8 2.123×10^4 _____

Write out how you would say each scientific notation.

9 32×10^{10} _____

_____

10 4.56×10^8 _____

_____

Pre-Algebra © 2004 Creative Teaching Press

Teeny-Tiny!

Rational	Scientific Notation
0.007	7×10^{-3}
0.000456	4.56×10^{-4}
0.00001234	1.234×10^{-5}

Express each number in scientific notation.

1 0.0000546

_____

2 0.00009832

_____

3 0.01357

_____

4 0.00030001

_____

5 0.0000005000

_____

6 0.000054321

_____

Express each scientific notation as a number.

7 1.45×10^{-8}

_____

8 6.1×10^{-10}

_____

9 3×10^{-8}

_____

10 5.0041×10^{-5}

_____

11 2.0005×10^{-6}

_____

12 4.321×10^{-3}

_____

Multiplying Extreme Numbers

$(2.1 \times 10^{10}) \times (3.4 \times 10^3) =$

Reorder $(2.1 \times 10^{10}) \times (3.4 \times 10^3) = 2.1 \times 3.4 \times 10^{10} \times 10^3$
Regroup $2.1 \times 3.4 \times 10^{10} \times 10^3 = (2.1 \times 3.4) \times (10^{10} \times 10^3)$
Multiply $(2.1 \times 3.4) \times (10^{10} \times 10^3) = 7.14 \times 10^{13}$

Evaluate each expression.

1 $(3.6 \times 10^8) \times (2 \times 10^8) =$

_____

2 $(5 \times 10^{-5}) \times (4.1 \times 10^{-3}) =$

_____

3 $(2.5 \times 10^5) \times (3.1 \times 10^{-5}) =$

_____

4 $(3.21 \times 10^{-3}) \times (2.31 \times 10^7) =$

_____

5 $(4.2 \times 10^5) \times (3 \times 10^6) =$

_____

6 $(7 \times 10^6) \times (3.56 \times 10^{-3}) =$

_____

7 $(0.2 \times 10^5) \times (6.7 \times 10^{-5}) =$

_____

8 $(5.4 \times 10^4) \times (0.1 \times 10^{-6}) =$

_____

9 $(0.09 \times 10^5) \times (0.01 \times 10^3) \times (200 \times 10^{-7}) =$

_____

10 $(2.15 \times 10^5) \times (3.4 \times 10^3) \times (3.4 \times 10^{-8}) =$

_____

Pre-Algebra © 2004 Creative Teaching Press

Putting It Together

Review

Fill in the blanks.

1 **Ratio:** Represents the relationship of two quantities that have _____.

2 **Rate:** Represents the relationship of two quantities that have _____.

3 **Proportion:** An equation that sets two _____ equal to each other.

4 _____: An expression that has a base and an exponent. The base is multiplied by itself the number of times as the exponent.

5 **Square Number:** This is a special power in which the exponent is _____.

6 **Square Roots:** The square root of a number is such a number that when squared equals _____.

7 _____: A mathematical procedure to evaluate an expression involving more than one mathematical operation.

8 **Estimate:** Calculate an amount _____ to the actual amount.

Answer the questions.

9 Is $\dfrac{1000 \text{ points}}{4 \text{ games}}$ a ratio or a rate? _____

10 Solve: $\dfrac{250}{750} = \dfrac{}{36}$

11 $\sqrt{49} =$ _____

12 $2^5 =$ _____

13 $[3 \times (7 - 3)] \div (33 - 21) =$ _____

Express each number in scientific notation.

14 2,340,000 _____

15 0.000050000 _____

16 2,340,000 × 0.00005000 _____

Additional Practice

REVIEW

Write the vocabulary word for each definition.

1 An expression that has a base and an exponent. _____

2 This is a special power in which the exponent is two. _____

3 Denoted by the radical symbol $\left(\sqrt{}\right)$. _____

4 A mathematical procedure to evaluate an expression involving more than one mathematical operation. _____

5 Represents the relationship of two quantities that have different units of measure. _____

6 Represents the relationship of two quantities that have the same units of measure. _____

7 A short form of writing numbers where the number is written as **n × 10ˣ** where **n** is a rational number from 1 to 9. _____

8 Calculate an amount close to the actual amount. _____

Answer the questions.

9 Is $\dfrac{160 \text{ inches}}{14 \text{ feet}}$ a ratio or a rate? _____

10 Solve: $\dfrac{}{56} = \dfrac{99}{88}$

11 $\sqrt{144}$ = _____

12 4^3 = _____

13 $[3^2 \times (4 + 3)] \div (2^3 + 1)$ = _____

Express each number in scientific notation.

14 12,340,000 _____

15 0.000030 _____

16 12,340,000 × 0.000030 _____

Pre-Algebra © 2004 Creative Teaching Press

Understanding Variables

Variable: A letter used to represent one or more numbers.

The age of a student is 25 years less than 40.
$$A = 40 - 25$$

The length times the height of the box is 30 in^2.
$$L \times H = 30 \text{ in}^2$$

Write an equation with variables to represent each unknown value.

1 The time it took to read a book, two hours, is equal
to the number of pages times seconds. _____

2 The product is nine multiplied by five. _____

3 The diameter is equal to the product of two and the radius. _____

4 The salary of the teacher is equal to the
monthly earnings times twelve. _____

5 The age of the sister is the brother's age plus 2 years. _____

6 The area of the square is the length of one side squared. _____

7 The unit rate is equal to the total cost, thirty dollars,
divided by the number of units. _____

8 The number of hours is equal to the quotient
of the number of minutes and sixty. _____

9 The perimeter of a square is the product of four
and the length of one side. _____

10 The perimeter of a rectangle is the product of two
and the sum of the length and width. _____

Equations with Variables

The variable *A* may represent area.
The variable *C* may represent circumference.
The number of boys may be represented by the variable *B*.

$$3 \cdot 4 = 12 \qquad (3)(4) = 12 \qquad 3x = 12$$

Note: Avoid using × to symbolize multiplication in an equation with variables. This avoids confusion with the variable x.

Write an equation with variables to represent each unknown value.

1 The number of girls equals the number of boys plus two. _____

2 The value of the number is the sum of 5 and 6. _____

3 The difference is 10 – 5. _____

4 The number of marbles in the bag is equal to 100 minus two that fell out. _____

5 The number of dots on a die is equal to the sum of each side. _____

6 The number of consumed calories is the total calories divided by the number of servings. _____

7 The sale price equals the original price minus the discount price. _____

8 The total cost is $500 multiplied by 1.06. _____

9 The time to read a book equals the number of pages times time to read one page. _____

10 The number of swings equals the number of swing sets multiplied by the number of swings per set. _____

Common Algebra Terms

Operations: A calculation by mathematical methods.
Variable: A letter used to represent one or more numbers.
Terms: The individual parts of the expression.
Like Terms: Terms that may be combined.
Coefficients: The numbers in the terms.
Expressions: A collection of numbers, variables, and operations.

Complete the chart.

Expression	4y − 5x • 7 + 3y	x + 2x + 3x + 4x	3 • 4 − 6y + 2y + x + 2x
Operations	subtraction multiplication addition		
Variables		x	
Terms			
Like Terms			
Coefficients			

Write It!

> The number of boys in the class is two more than the number of girls.
>
> B = 2 + G

Read the problem. Circle the unknown, box the numbers, and underline the operations. Then write an equation using the appropriate variables.

1 The total pay is the product of hours
worked and hourly rate. _____

2 The interest earned is equal to the principal
multiplied by the interest rate multiplied by the time. _____

3 The distance is equal to the product
of the rate of speed and time. _____

4 The weight of the cat is the difference of the
weight of the dog and twenty pounds. _____

5 The cost of one candy bar is equal to one dollar divided by two. _____

6 The y-value is equal to the product of the slope
and x-value and then added to the y-intercept. _____

7 The square of x is equal to x multiplied by x. _____

8 The area of a circle is equal to pi times the radius squared. _____

9 The length of the hypotenuse squared
equals the sum of each side squared. _____

10 The number of students receiving an A on the test
was equal to 15% of the total number of students. _____

Pre-Algebra © 2004 Creative Teaching Press

Investigation

Draw a model of each expression. Add like terms. Rewrite the expression.

1 3x + 5y + 4y + 3x + 5 + 2 _____

2 3y + 5 + 4x + 3x + 5 + 2y _____

3 3y + 5x + 4y + 3y + 5x + 2x _____

4 3 + 5y + 4x + 3x + 5 + 2 _____

5 4 + 9x + 8 + 3x − 2y + 8y _____

6 7 × 5 + (6x • 5x) − 8 _____

7 21 − 14x + 7y + 8 + 3y − 2x _____

8 4x(2x + 3x) + 5y(5y + 3y) _____

Distribute It!

Distributive Property: The product of a number and a sum is equal to the sum of the number multiplied by each number added in the sum.

$5 \times (3 + 6) = 5 \times 3 + 5 \times 6$

$5(x + y) = 5x + 5y$

We can prove this true with the *Order of Operations.*

$5 \times (3 + 6) = 5 \times 3 + 5 \times 6$
$5 \times (9) = 15 + 30$
$45 = 45$

$3x + 4x + 7 =$
$7x + 7$ or $7(x + 1)$

Use the distributive property to simplify each mathematical expression. Show your work.

1 $7(100 + 70)$

_____

2 $5(x + 4)$

_____

3 $(x + y)6$

_____

4 $5(100 + x + y)$

_____

5 $10(3x + 12 + z)$

_____

6 $(a + b)6 + 3(2a + b)$

_____

7 $a + a + b$

_____

8 $x + 2x + 5x$

_____

9 $5x + 3x + 3$

_____

10 $8x + 2x + 5$

_____

Name _____   Date _____

Adding Like Terms

Simplified Expression: An expression that has all like terms combined.

$$5x + 4x = x(5 + 4) = 9x$$

Simplify.

1 $2a + 3a$

_____

2 $5y + 3y + 3$

_____

3 $4z + 3p + 4z + 5$

_____

4 $8r + 5r + 6$

_____

5 $5x + 2x + 3x + 4x$

_____

6 $3b + 4b + 5b + 6b$

_____

7 $3y + 4y + 5x + 6x$

_____

8 $10y + 13 + 25x + 6y + 5x$

_____

9 $5(6a + 4) + 10a + 4a + 3$

_____

10 $3(9y + 5x) + 2(7y + 8x) + 6$

_____

11 $2(7y + 4x + 2z) + 2(6y + 9x + 5z)$

_____

12 $25y + 52x + 15z + 7(6y + 3x + 4z) + 10y + 9x + 12z$

_____

13 $5(6 + 3x + 4y) + 3(9z + 3x + 5y)$

_____

14 $2x + 3x + 4 + 5z + 6y + 7x + 8 + 9x + 10z + 11y + 12x + 13y$

_____

Simplify It!

$5x - 3x = 2x$

$3x + 5y + 4z + 10$ **not** $10 + 5y + 4z + 3x$

Simplify.

1 $6y + 7y$

_____

2 $10a - 3a$

_____

3 $5x - 2x - 3x + 4x$

_____

4 $3a - 4b - 5a + 6b$

_____

5 $5y - y + 10x - 3x$

_____

6 $x + 25x - 6y + 5y - 11$

_____

7 $8z - 5f + 6 + 6f - 3z$

_____

8 $5(x + 2y) - 5y$

_____

9 $10 + 3(5a - 5a) + 10a + 3$

_____

10 $25y + 52x + 15z - 7(6y + 3x - 4z) + 10y - 9x - 12z$

_____

11 $5y - y + 10x - 3x + 5(x + 2y) - 5y$

_____

12 $10(a - 3a) + 2(10 + 5a) + 10a - 4(a + 3)$

_____

Pre-Algebra © 2004 Creative Teaching Press

Evaluate

Evaluate 5a + 6a if a = 3
5(3) + 6(3) = 33

Evaluate each expression with the given values.

	a = 2	a = ‾2	a = $\frac{1}{2}$
1 3a – 4a			
2 5a – 6 + 3a			
3 ‾a + 4a			
4 $\frac{a}{2}$ + a			
5 $\frac{4}{a}$ • $\frac{a}{4}$			
6 $\frac{1}{3}$a + 5			
7 $\frac{1}{2}$a – $\frac{3}{4}$a			
8 ‾2a • a(4 – 4)			
9 8a ÷ a			
10 6(a + 5) + 4			

Equations and Solutions

Equations that contain variables are called **open sentences**. When a variable is replaced by a number, the statement is either true or it is false. A true statement is a **solution**.

If $x + 2 = 2$, then 0 is a solution and 3 is not a solution.

Complete each statement by writing *is a solution* or *is not a solution*.

1 If $x + 3 = 4$, then 1 _____

2 If $x + 3 = 4$, then 2 _____

3 If $x + 1 = 1$, then 0 _____

4 If $x + 1 = 1$, then $1\frac{1}{2}$ _____

5 If $x + 2 = 3$, then 1 _____

6 If $x + 2 = 3$, then 2 _____

7 If $x + 3 = 5$, then 2 _____

8 If $x + 3 = 5$, then 1 _____

9 If $x + 4 = 4$, then 1 _____

10 If $x + 4 = 4$, then 0 _____

11 If $x + 0 = 4$, then 4 _____

12 If $x + 0 = 4$, then 1 _____

13 If $x + 1 = 0$, then 0 _____

14 If $x + 1 = 0$, then 1 _____

15 If $x + 1 = 0$, then 2 _____

Undoing

If you move three whole numbers to the right on the number line ($^+$3),
how do you get back to where you started?

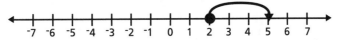

You do the inverse operation with the same value ($^-$3).

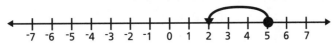

Draw a line from each operation and value on the left to the matching inverse on the right.

1 + 4   **A.** ÷ ($^-$4)

2 − 8   **B.** + 1.03

3 × 3   **C.** + 4

4 ÷ 9   **D.** − 253

5 + ($^-$4)   **E.** − 4

6 ÷ 0.2   **F.** × 9

7 − 1.03   **G.** + 8

8 + 253   **H.** − 15

9 + $\frac{5}{2}$ **I.** × 3

10 ÷ 3   **J.** ÷ 3

11 × ($^-$4)   **K.** × 0.2

12 + 15   **L.** − 2$\frac{1}{2}$

More to Undo

> **Inverse Operations:** Operations that undo one another.

Answer each question.

1 If you start at 4 and subtract 2, how do you get back to 4 using the inverse operation? _____

2 If you start at 5 and multiply by 3, how do you get back to 5 using the inverse operation? _____

3 If you start at 10 and divide by 2, how do you get back to 10 using the inverse operation? _____

4 If you start at ⁻8 and divide by 2, how do you get back to ⁻8 using the inverse operation? _____

5 If you start at 6 and add ⁻2, how do you get back to 6 using the inverse operation? _____

6 Fill in the chart.

Operation	Inverse
add	
subtract	
multiply	
divide	

Solve for *a* using an inverse operation. Show your work.

7 State the inverse operation. $\dfrac{a}{2} = 4$ _____

8 State the inverse operation. $a \times 3 = 12$ _____

9 State the inverse operation. $a \times 5 = 6$ _____

Pre-Algebra © 2004 Creative Teaching Press

Solving Equations with Addition

$$x + 2 = 4$$
$$x + 2 - 2 = 4 - 2$$
$$x + 0 = 2$$
$$x = 2$$

Solve. Show every step.

1 $a + 5 = 6$

2 $x + 7 = 20$

3 $z + 11 = 50$

4 $b + 5 = 13$

5 $y + 9 = 16$

6 $x + 5 + 6 = 13$

7 $y + 5 = 3$

8 $z + (^-4) = 6$

9 $a + 4 + 7 = 9$

Pre-Algebra © 2004 Creative Teaching Press

Subtraction Solutions

$$x - 2 = 4$$
$$x - 2 + \mathbf{2} = 4 + \mathbf{2}$$
$$x + 0 = 6$$
$$x = 6$$

Solve. Show every step.

1 $a - 5 = 6$

2 $x - 10 = 20$

3 $z - 11 = 20$

4 $b - 7 = 13$

5 $y - 9 = 16$

6 $x - 5 - 6 = 13$

7 $y - 5 = {}^{-}3$

8 $z - ({}^{-}4) = 6$

Pre-Algebra © 2004 Creative Teaching Press

Multiplication Solutions

$$y \cdot 2 = 4$$
$$y \cdot 2 \div 2 = 4 \div 2$$
$$y \cdot 1 = 2$$
$$y = 2$$

Solve. Show every step.

1 $a \cdot 5 = 10$

2 $x \cdot 10 = 20$

3 $z \cdot 11 = 44$

4 $b \cdot 7 = 28$

5 $y \cdot 9 = 72$

6 $x \cdot 15 = 75$

7 $y \cdot 5 = 12$

8 $z \cdot (^-4) = 6$

Division Solutions

$$x \div 2 = 4$$
$$x \div 2 \cdot \mathbf{2} = 4 \cdot \mathbf{2}$$
$$x \div 1 = 8$$
$$x = 8$$

Solve. Show your work.

1 $a \div 3 = 4$

2 $x \div 10 = 2$

3 $z \div 11 = 3$

4 $b \div 7 = 4$

5 $y \div 9 = 8$

6 $x \div 6 = 5$

7 $y \div 4 = {}^-2$

8 $z \div {}^-4 = 3$

Pre-Algebra © 2004 Creative Teaching Press

All Together

Solve.

1 $y \div 4 = ^-8$

2 $x + 10 = 12$

3 $a - 9 = 16$

4 $2y = ^-10$

5 $y \div 7 = ^-56$

6 $3y = ^-12$

7 $b - 4 = ^-7$

8 $y \div ^-6 = 24$

9 $z + ^-5 = ^-7$

10 $2a \div 4 = 3$

11 $5y \times 5 = 30$

12 $3x + 5x = 2x + 2$

13 $4x + 3 = 23$

14 $7x + 8 = 57$

15 $\dfrac{3x}{4} + 11 = 22 - 5$

16 $\dfrac{36}{x} = 18$

Educational Equations

Solve. Then write the variable letter above the corresponding value on the lines below to finish the quote.

1 $5 \cdot I = 5$

I = ____

2 $^-2 \cdot D = {}^-18$

D = ____

3 $30 \div T = 15$

T = ____

4 $5 + S = 8$

S = ____

5 $^-5 \cdot E = {}^-35$

E = ____

6 $3 \cdot A = 12$

A = ____

7 $V - 10 = {}^-2$

V = ____

8 $10 - C = 5$

C = ____

9 $H \div 2 = 3$

H = ____

"Education is not received . . .

____ ____ ____ ____ ____ ____ ____ ____ ____ ____ ____ ____."
 1   2   1   3   4   5   6   1   7   8   7   9

Pre-Algebra © 2004 Creative Teaching Press

Proportions

Proportion: An equation that sets two ratios equal to each other.

$$\frac{a}{4} = \frac{1}{2}$$

$$\frac{2}{4} = \frac{1}{2}$$

Solve.

1 $\dfrac{a}{5} = \dfrac{8}{10}$

2 $\dfrac{1}{3} = \dfrac{4}{d}$

3 $\dfrac{2}{10} = \dfrac{c}{5}$

4 $\dfrac{24}{80} = \dfrac{x}{60}$

5 $\dfrac{1}{b} = \dfrac{4}{16}$

6 $\dfrac{50}{100} = \dfrac{10}{d}$

7 $\dfrac{3}{b} = \dfrac{6}{16}$

8 $\dfrac{a}{9} = \dfrac{2}{6}$

9 $\dfrac{a}{5} = \dfrac{8}{10}$

10 $\dfrac{6}{24} = \dfrac{2}{d}$

11 $\dfrac{20}{x} = \dfrac{16}{36}$

12 $\dfrac{10}{16} = \dfrac{x}{56}$

Advanced Proportions

Cross Product Property: Given two equivalent ratios, $\frac{a}{b}$ and $\frac{c}{d}$, the cross product property states that $a \times d = b \times c$.

$$\frac{a}{2} = \frac{3}{4}$$

$$a \times 4 = 3 \times 2$$

$$a \times 4 = 6$$

$a \times 4 = 6$ ▲ $a \times 4 \div 4 = 6 \div 4$ ▲

$$a = \frac{3}{2}$$

Use the cross product property to solve the equations.

1 $\dfrac{4}{6} = \dfrac{3}{d}$

2 $\dfrac{6}{b} = \dfrac{3}{5}$

3 $\dfrac{1}{b} = \dfrac{4}{16}$

4 $\dfrac{1}{3} = \dfrac{c}{24}$

5 $\dfrac{a}{7} = \dfrac{14}{49}$

6 $\dfrac{a}{3} = \dfrac{2}{6}$

7 $\dfrac{4}{10} = \dfrac{6}{d}$

8 $\dfrac{11}{12} = \dfrac{22}{d}$

9 $\dfrac{15}{4} = \dfrac{x}{20}$

10 $\dfrac{6}{a} = \dfrac{4}{32}$

11 $\dfrac{x}{6} = \dfrac{55}{66}$

12 $\dfrac{5}{a} = \dfrac{45}{54}$

Discovery

Evaluate each statement. Write *True* if the equation balances. Write *False* if it does not.

1 $5 + 6 = 6 + 5$ _____

2 $(2 + 3) + 4 = 2 + (3 + 4)$ _____

3 $4 - 3 = 3 - 4$ _____

4 $(10 - 7) - 4 = 10 - (7 - 4)$ _____

5 $7 \times 6 = 6 \times 7$ _____

6 $(2 \times 4) \times 3 = 2 \times (4 \times 3)$ _____

7 $30 \div 3 = 3 \div 30$ _____

8 $(9 \div 3) \div 2 = 9 \div (3 \div 2)$ _____

Based on the previous exercises, determine if the following mathematical statements are true or false for any number x, y, and z. Write *True* or *False* for each statement.

9 $x + y = y + x$ _____

10 $(x + y) + z = x + (y + z)$ _____

11 $x - y = y - x$ _____

12 $(x - y) - z = x - (y - z)$ _____

13 $x \bullet y = y \bullet x$ _____

14 $(x \bullet y)z = x(y \bullet z)$ _____

15 $x \div y = y \div x$ _____

16 $(x \div y) \div z = \dfrac{y \div z}{x}$ _____

Associative and Commutative Properties

Associative Property of Addition: Changing the grouping of the addends does not change the sum.

$$(3 + 4) + 2 = 3 + (4 + 2)$$

Commutative Property of Addition: Changing the order of the addends does not change the sum.

$$3 + 4 = 4 + 3$$

Associative Property of Multiplication: Changing the grouping of the factors does not change the product.

$$(3 \times 4) \times 2 = 3 \times (4 \times 2)$$

Commutative Property of Multiplication: Changing the order of the factors does not change the product.

$$3 \times 4 = 4 \times 3$$

State the property that proves each statement is true. If the statement is NOT true, explain why.

1 $x + y = y + x$ _____

2 $(x + y) + z = x + (y + z)$ _____

3 $x - y = y - x$ _____

4 $(x - y) - z = x - (y - z)$ _____

5 $x \bullet y = y \bullet x$ _____

6 $(x \bullet y)z = x(y \bullet z)$ _____

7 $x \div y = y \div x$ _____

8 $(x \div y) \div z = x \div (y \div z)$ _____

Shortcuts

Product Property: When multiplying powers having the same base, add the exponents.
$$a^2 \times a^3 = a^{2+3} = a^5$$

Power Property: When finding the power of a power, multiply the exponents.
$$(a^2)^3 = a^{2 \times 3} = a^6$$

Solve.

1 $a^6 \times a^3 =$ _____

2 $(b^2)^4 =$ _____

3 $y^5 \times y^7 =$ _____

4 $(z^5)^5 =$ _____

5 $(a^6)^4 =$ _____

6 $b^5 \times b^2 =$ _____

7 $a^3 \times a^{10} =$ _____

8 $(y^5)^2 =$ _____

9 $b^4 \times b^5 =$ _____

10 $(a^2)^{10} =$ _____

11 $a^{-4} \times a^5 =$ _____

12 $(a^{-3})^{-3} =$ _____

13 $a^2 \times a^{-2} =$ _____

14 $y^2 \times y^3 =$ _____

Without actually solving the expressions, determine the relationship of the following and write the correct symbol in the circle to make it true.

15 $a^3 \times a^{10}$ ◯ $(a^3)^4$

16 $a^5 \times a^1$ ◯ $(a^1)^5$

17 $a^{-3} \times a^3$ ◯ $(a^1)^1$

18 $a^0 \times a^{100}$ ◯ $(a^{10})^{10}$

Pre-Algebra © 2004 Creative Teaching Press

Division Property of Exponents

Division Property: When dividing powers having the same base, subtract the exponents.

$$a^4 \div a^2 = a^{4-2} = a^2 \qquad \frac{a^4}{a^2} = a^{4-2} = a^2$$

Simplify the expressions.

1 $a^6 \div a^3 =$

2 $\dfrac{b^4}{b^2} =$

3 $y^8 \div y^7 =$

4 $\dfrac{b^6}{b^2} =$

5 $\dfrac{y^5}{y^3} =$

6 $z^5 \div z^2 =$

7 $a^{10} \div a^3 =$

8 $\dfrac{y^7}{y^3} =$

9 $z^{125} \div z^{119} =$

10 $\dfrac{b^{257}}{b^{236}} =$

11 $a^{576} \div a^{572} =$

12 $\dfrac{b^2}{b^2} =$

13 $a^2 \div a^{-2} =$

14 $a^2 \div y^{-3} =$

Simplify the expression. Then find the answer.

15 $2^{99} \div 2^{95} =$

16 $3^{57} \div 3^{56} =$

17 $765^{50} \div 765^{50} =$

18 $3^2 \div 2^1 =$

Pre-Algebra © 2004 Creative Teaching Press

Simplifying Polynomials

Polynomial: An expression in which each term is of the form ax^b.
A polynomial is written so that the value of the exponents in each expression decrease from left to right.

Standard form: $3x^4 + 5x^2 + x + 10$
NOT standard form: $10 + x + 5x^2 + 3x^4$

For each polynomial circle *standard* or *not standard*. If the polynomial is not standard, write it in standard form.

1 $x^2 + x^6 + x^3$ standard not standard

2 $5x^3 + 4x^2 + 3x + 9$ standard not standard

3 $2x^7 + x^5 + 3x + 5 + 4x^2$ standard not standard

4 $3x^9 + x^5 + 4x + x^8 + 3x^3 + 5$ standard not standard

5 $7x^6 + x^5 + x^4 + 3x^3 + 12$ standard not standard

6 $100 + 50x^6 + 12x^2 + 3x^3$ standard not standard

7 $5x + 5x^2 + 5x^4 + 5x^3 + 5$ standard not standard

8 $100x^{100} + 50x^{50} + 4x^4 + 3x^3$ standard not standard

9 $4x^4 + x^3 + x^7 + 3x^3 + 12$ standard not standard

10 $15 + 2x^6 + x^5 + x^5 + 3x^6 + 12$ standard not standard

Pre-Algebra © 2004 Creative Teaching Press

Monomials, Binomials, and Trinomials

Monomial: Polynomials that have only one term when simplified. **Examples:** 3, 3x, $3x^4$
Binomial: Polynomials that have two terms when simplified. **Examples:** $3x + 3$, $3x^5 + 3x^4$
Trinomials: Polynomials that have three terms when simplified. **Example:** $3x^3 + 3x^2 + 3x$

Put a check under the column that names the polynomial.

	Monomial	Binomial	Trinomial
1 6			
2 $3x^2 + 3x^2 + 3x$			
3 $3x^4$			
4 $5z$			
5 $7y^7 + 2y^5 + 8$			
6 $a + 5$			
7 $456b$			
8 $3x^3 + 3x^2 + 3x$			
9 $3y^5 + 6$			
10 $3 + 7$			

Pre-Algebra © 2004 Creative Teaching Press

More Polynomials

For each exercise simplify the expression and name the type of polynomial.

1 $3 + 5x^3 + 2x^2 + 10$

_____

_____

2 $z + 2z + 3z$

_____

_____

3 $b + 3 + 2b + 4$

_____

_____

4 $\sqrt{9} - 3 + z$

_____

_____

5 $2 \cdot 3 + z \cdot z$

_____

_____

6 $2(a^3 + 4a) + 3a$

_____

_____

7 $2x^3 + x(x^2 + 4x)$

_____

_____

8 $2y^3 + 5y(4y^2 + 6y)$

_____

_____

9 $x^3 \div x^2 + 10x + 6$

_____

_____

10 $2^3 - 5y(4y^2 + 6y)$

_____

_____

11 $7 + 5x^3 + 2x^2 + 10 - 3 + 4x^3$

_____

_____

12 $6(3a^3 + 2a) + 10$

_____

_____

13 $2x^3 + x(x^2 + 4x) + 2x^3$

_____

_____

14 $y^4 + 4y^2(7y^2 + 12y)$

_____

_____

15 $x^8 \div x^6 + 9x + 16$

_____

_____

16 $\sqrt{16} - 2[5y(4y^2 + 6y)]$

_____

_____

Evaluating Simple Expressions

$$5x - 2x - 3x + 4x; \ x = 2$$
$$(5x - 2x - 3x) + 4x = 0 + 4x = 4x$$
$$4x = 4(2)$$
$$4(2) = 8$$

Evaluate the following expressions when a = 0, b = 2, c = 3, and d = 1.

1 $a - b - a + c$

_____

2 $d + 2a - 3b$

_____

3 $5d - a + b + c$

_____

4 $\dfrac{d}{c} - b^c$

_____

Evaluate the following expressions when a = 3, b = 5, and c = 3.

5 $3a - 2b - 2a$

_____

6 $5a - 2b - 3a + 4c$

_____

7 $a + 2b - 3a + 4$

_____

8 $2(5a - 2b) - 3(3a + 4)$

_____

9 $5(9a - 6b + 3) + 2(3a + 4) + 10$

_____

10 $1a + 25a - 6b + 5b - 11c$

_____

11 $25 + 2(5a - 5a) + 10a - 4a + 3b$

_____

12 $2c + 5a + 4b + 3(a + 3b - 4c) + 4b - 7b - 3a$

_____

Crossword Vocabulary

REVIEW

Use the clues to complete the puzzle.

Across

2. An equation that sets two ratios equal
5. A true statement
7. Terms that may be combined
8. A letter used to represent one or more numbers
10. A statement formed when an equality is placed between two expressions
11. A collection of numbers, variables, and operations
12. Operations that undo one another

Down

1. The individual parts of an expression
2. An expression in which every term is of the form ax^b
3. Calculations by mathematical methods
4. The numbers in the terms
6. An expression that has all like terms combined
9. Equations with variables

Algebra Basics

REVIEW

In exercises 1 and 2, circle the unknown, box the numbers, and underline the operations. Then write an equation using appropriate variables.

1 The number of A grades is 5 less than the number of B grades in the class.

_____

2 The exterior angle of a triangle is the sum of the two nonadjacent interior angles.

_____

State the property that proves the following expression or give an example to disprove it.

3 $(x + y) + z = x + (y + z)$ _____

4 $x - y = y - x$ _____

5 $y \cdot z = z \cdot y$ _____

6 State the property that may be used to simplify the following and simplify: $5(x + 4)$

_____

Solve.

7 $y \div 4 = {}^-8$ **8** $x + 10 = 12$ **9** $\dfrac{a}{10} = \dfrac{4}{5}$

Simplify and state the type of polynomial.

10 $2y^3 \cdot 4y^2 + 6y$ _____   **11** $(z^3 \div z^2) \cdot z^5$ _____

_____   _____

12 $a^3 \div a^2 + 10a + 10$ _____   **13** $2^3 - 5y(4y^2 + 6y)$ _____

_____   _____

Evaluate the following expressions when $a = 1$, $b = 2$, $c = 3$, and $d = 4$.

14 $7a - 2b - 3a + 4c$ **15** $d + 2b - (3a + 1)$ **16** $^-5(a - 2b) - 3(3a + 4)$

More Algebra Basics

REVIEW

In exercises 1 and 2, circle the unknown, box the numbers, and underline the operations. Then write an equation using appropriate variables.

1 The volume of a cube is the length of one side to the third power.

_____

2 The sale price is the original price multiplied by the difference of the discount % and 100%.

_____

State the property that proves the following expression or give an example to disprove it.

3 $(x - y) - z = x - (y - z)$ _____

4 $xy = yx$ _____

5 $y \div z = z \div y$ _____

6 State the property that may be used to simplify the following; simplify: $4x + 7x + 11$

_____

Solve.

7 $y \cdot {}^-8 = {}^-24$ **8** $x - 9 = 6$ **9** $\dfrac{a}{9} = \dfrac{3}{10}$

Simplify and state the type of polynomial.

10 $y^3 \cdot y^2 + y$ _____   **11** $(z^8 \cdot z^6) \div z^4$ _____

12 $a^3 \times a^2 \times 10a \times 10$ _____   **13** $3y^2(y + y) + y^2 + 15$ _____

Evaluate the following expressions when $a = 0$, $b = 2$, $c = 3$, and $d = 1$.

14 $a - b - a + c$ **15** $d + 2a - 3b$ **16** $5d - a + b + c$

Pre-Algebra © 2004 Creative Teaching Press

Reciprocals

$$\frac{1}{2}a = 2$$

$$\frac{1}{2} \cdot \frac{2}{1} a = 2 \cdot \frac{2}{1}$$

$$a = 4$$

Solve. Show your work.

1 $\frac{1}{3}z = 22$

2 $-\frac{1}{4}b = 12$

3 $\frac{1}{5}y = 32$

4 $-\frac{1}{5}c = {}^-9$

5 $\frac{1}{6}y = {}^-14$

6 $\frac{1}{8}z = 6$

7 $-\frac{2}{3}b = 9$

8 $-\frac{4}{5}y = {}^-12$

9 $\frac{2}{3}a = \frac{5}{4}$

10 $\frac{3}{4}y + 6 = 12$

11 $\frac{a}{2} = \frac{1}{2}$

12 $\frac{c}{4} = 2$

Pre-Algebra © 2004 Creative Teaching Press

Complex Equations

$$\frac{1}{2}a + 2 = 10$$

$$\frac{1}{2}a + 2 - 2 = 10 - 2$$

$$\frac{1}{2}a = 8$$

$$\frac{1}{2}(2)\,a = 8(2)$$

$$a = 16$$

Check: $\frac{1}{2}(16) + 2 = 10$

$$10 = 10$$

Solve.

1 $9 = {}^-3z + 4z$

2 $12 - 2a = 10$

3 $4b + 7 = 19$

4 $\frac{1}{3}z - \frac{1}{3} = 1$

5 $5(t + 3) = 45$

6 $8 = f(5) - 7$

7 $\frac{1}{2}(a + 8) = 6$

8 ${}^-7(d) + 12 = 68$

9 $4(a + 6) + 3 = 39$

10 $5(y + 7) + {}^-2(3 + y) = 23$

11 $1 = z(3 + 10) - 6z$

12 $5(p + 6) - 7(3 + p) = 5$

More Complex Equations

Solve.

1 $-28 = \dfrac{4}{x} - 12$

2 $3x + 8 = 35$

3 $\dfrac{x}{4} + 5x = 42$

4 $\dfrac{14}{x} + \dfrac{1}{x} + (2 \cdot 5) = 15$

5 $9 = \dfrac{x}{4} + 4$

6 $3x - 10 = 26$

7 $8 + 9x = 53$

8 $-10 = -6x + 4x$

9 $5(x + 8) - 4(3 + x) = 30$

10 $30 = \dfrac{x}{3x} \cdot 6x$

11 $2(x + 3) + {}^-3(3 + x) = {}^-15$

12 $4(x + 9) + 8 = 44$

13 $-5(x) + 12 = -38$

14 $\dfrac{1}{2}(x + 8) = 12$

15 $51 = x(7) - 5$

16 $5(x + 3) = 55$

17 $\dfrac{1}{2}x - \dfrac{1}{4} = 3\dfrac{3}{4}$

18 $3x + 7 = 31$

19 $12 - 2x = {}^-4$

20 $7 = x(3 + 10x) - 6x$

Pre-Algebra © 2004 Creative Teaching Press

Isolating Variables 1

$\frac{1}{2}a + 2a + 4 = 3(2 + a)$

$2\frac{1}{2}a + 4 = 6 + 3a$

$2\frac{1}{2}a - 3a + 4 = 6 + 3a - 3a$

$-\frac{1}{2}a + 4 = 6$

$-\frac{1}{2}a + 4 - 4 = 6 - 4$

$-\frac{1}{2}a = 2$

$-\frac{1}{2}(^-2)a = 2(^-2)$

$a = {}^-4$

Check: $\frac{1}{2}(^-4) + 2(^-4) + 4 = 3[2 + (^-4)]$

$^-6 = {}^-6$

Solve for the variable. Use a separate piece of paper if needed. Show your work. Check your solution.

1 $\frac{1}{3}b + 3(2) - 2b = {}^-8 + {}^-2b$

2 $2z + 4(z + 1) = 5 - 0z$

3 $4c - 3c + 7 = 2c + 10$

4 $7a - 8 = 24 + 3a$

5 $12(y + 2) = 3(2y - 4)$

6 $3(z + 2) + 4z = 28 - 2(z + 2)$

7 $\frac{1}{5}a + 4(2) + 4a = 5a$

8 $3x + 3(x + 1) = 4x - (6 + 7)$

9 $5y - 2y + 15 = 5y + (^-6 + 7)$

10 $\frac{30}{n} - 7n + 12 = {}^-7 - 18$

11 $8(x + 2) = 20(2x - 4)$

12 $3(a + 5) + 3a = 12a - 3(a - 3) - 2$

Isolating Variables 2

Solve for the variable. Use a separate piece of paper if needed. Show your work. Check your solution.

1 $4x - 9 = 5x + 7$

2 $5(^-x + 10) = 5x + 10$

3 $7x = 2(15 + x)$

4 $3x - 16 = {}^-41 + 8x$

5 $5x \cdot \dfrac{1}{5} = 3x \cdot \dfrac{1}{3}$

6 $3x + 10 = \dfrac{400}{x}$

7 $^-5x = 3(x + 4) + 2$

8 $3x + 15 = 4(x + 9) - 20$

9 $\dfrac{3}{x} = \dfrac{2(10x + 10)}{6(2 \bullet 50)}$

10 $\dfrac{1}{3}x + 12(2)\ {}^-2x = {}^-18 + 3x$

11 $5(y + 2) + 4y = 11y$

12 $4(n + 3) = 3(2n - 3) + 10$

Pre-Algebra © 2004 Creative Teaching Press

Multiple Transformations

R E V I E W

Complete the following statements with *is a solution* or *is not a solution*.

1 If $3b + 3(2b) = {}^-18$, then 2 _____.

2 If $4(a + 2a) = 12$, then 1 _____.

3 If $5(2z - 3) + 5 = 4z + 2$, then 2 _____.

4 If $2y - 3(y + 5) = 4(y + 3) - 2$, then 5 _____.

Solve for the variable. Show your work. Then check your solution.

5 $a - 4(a + 6) = 4a + 2(3 - 2a)$

6 ${}^-28 - 2(f + 3) = {}^-5(f - 1)$

7 $2(y + 4) - 6 = 3(5 + 3y)$

8 $\dfrac{z}{3} + 5 = \dfrac{z}{6}$

9 ${}^-2y = 16y - 9$

Advanced Concepts

REVIEW

$$x \div 2 = 4$$
$$x \div 2 \times 2 = 4 \times 2$$
$$x \div 1 = 8$$
$$x = 8$$

Solve for the variable using reciprocals. Show your work.

1 $-\frac{1}{5}y = {}^-10$

2 $\frac{3}{2}a = \frac{5}{4}$

3 $\frac{3}{4}y = 6$

Solve for the variable. Show your work. Then check your solution.

4 $^-18 = {}^-3(z + 4)$

5 $12 - 2a = 10$

6 $5y + 35 - 6 - 2y = 23$

7 $4(a + 3) = a + 6$

8 $12y = 4y - 24$

9 $6(2z + 5) - 30 = 12z$

Complete the following statements with *is a solution* or *is not a solution*.

10 If $3b + b = 4b$, then 7 _____.

11 If $6a - a = 5a$, then 3 _____.

12 If $12y - 6(2y) = 0$, then 1 _____.

Pre-Algebra © 2004 Creative Teaching Press

Name _____ Date _____

You Choose 1

Complete one of the following activities:

1. The different number groups have specific symbols in mathematics. Look up number groups and symbols in a book or on the Internet and make a display below that illustrates each.

OR

2. List five unique situations when each of the following seems most appropriate to use: fractions, whole numbers, percents, and decimals.

Use the space below for notes.

You Choose 2

Complete one of the following activities:

1. Fractions are used in many areas besides mathematics. One of these areas is music.
   Explain how fractions are important in music and give the fraction equivalents for different notes.

OR

2. Write out all of the pre-algebra vocabulary words and definitions and give an example of each word.

Use the space below for notes.

Answer Key

Number Chat (page 5)

1. decimal
2. whole number
3. decimal or fraction
4. decimal or whole number
5. fraction or whole number (30 minutes)
6. whole number
7. fraction
8. decimal
9. whole number
10. decimal
11. decimal
12. fraction

Naming Number Sets (page 6)

1. accept: any integer less than 0
2. accept: any rational number between 3 and 4
3. accept: any integer between 0 and ⁻5
4. ⁻1/2
5. 59
6. ⁻5
7. 10
8. irrational number
9. integer
10. rational number
11. integer
12. rational number or integer

Math Operations (page 7)

1. $4 \times 4 = 16$
2. $\$350 \div 7 = \$50$
3. $\$30 - \$22 = \$8$
4. $10 + 20 + 14 + 13 + 30 + 12 + 24 + 4 + 2 + 3 = 132$
5. $50 - 25 = 25$ and $50 + 25 = 75$
6. $2 \times 4 \times 6 = 48$
7. $6 \times 6 = 36$
8. $36 - (5 \times 7) = 1$

Vocabulary Practice (page 8)

1. Integers
2. Whole
3. Naturals
4. Rationals
5. Set
6. Digits
7. Fraction
8. Sum
9. Product
10. Difference
11. Quotient

Crossword (page 9)

Across
2. irrational
4. fractions
6. quotient
9. integers
11. product
12. decimal
13. sum

Down
1. difference
3. rational
5. whole
7. natural
8. digits
10. set

Clue Words (page 10)

Answers will vary. Possible answers include:

1. more than, counted
2. smaller than, reduced by
3. grow, compounded
4. sectioned, split

Looking for Clues (page 11)

1. tally +
2. less than −
3. magnified ×
4. total +, more than +
5. partitioned ÷, counted with +
6. deduct −
7. take −
8. extra +
9. count +, except −

Using Clue Words (page 12)

Answers will vary.

Looking for Remainders (page 13)

1. Yes	2. No	3. Yes
4. No	5. Yes	6. Yes
7. Yes	8. No	9. Yes
10. No	11. Yes	12. No

Divisibility Tests (page 14)

1. Yes: 2, 3, 4, 6, 8, 9	2. Yes: 2, 3, 4, 6, 8, 9
3. Yes: 2, 3, 4, 5, 6, 8, 10	4. Yes: 2, 3, 4, 5, 6, 8, 9, 10
5. Yes: 2, 3, 4, 6, 8, 9	6. Yes: 3, 9

7. 0, 2, 4, 6, 8
8. 2, 5, 8
9. 2, 6
10. 2, 6

Factors (page 15)

1. 1, 42, 2, 21, 3, 14, 6, 7
2. 1, 77, 7, 11
3. 1, 210, 2, 105, 3, 70, 5, 42, 6, 35, 7, 30, 10, 21, 14, 15
4. 1, 126, 2, 63, 3, 42, 6, 21, 7, 18, 9, 14
5. 1, 50, 2, 25, 5, 10
6. 1, 200, 2, 100, 4, 50, 5, 40
7. 1, 143, 11, 13
8. 1, 58, 2, 29
9. 1, 61
10. 1, 89

Common Factors (page 16)

1. 1, 7
2. 1, 2, 4
3. 1, 3, 9
4. 1 (both prime)
5. 1 (both prime)
6. 1, 2, 4
7. 1, 2, 4, 8
8. 1, 7
9. 1, 2, 5, 10, 25, 50
10. 1, 2, 3, 4, 6, 12

Greatest Common Factor (page 17)

1. 7
2. 42
3. 7
4. 43
5. 1 (all prime)
6. 5
7. 15
8. 3
9. 19
10. 3

Multiples (page 18)

1. 5, 10, 15, 20, 25, 30, 35, 40, 45, 50
2. 6, 12, 18, 24, 30, 36, 42, 48, 54, 60
3. Possible Answer: 30, 60, 90
4. 30
5. 7, 14, 21, 28, 35, 42, 49, 56, 63, 70
6. 14, 28, 42, 56, 70, 84, 98, 112, 126, 140
7. Possible Answer: 14, 28, 42
8. 14

Factors and Multiples (page 19)

1. D
2. C
3. G
4. A
5. J
6. F
7. B
8. H
9. I
10. E

Prime and Composite Numbers (page 20)

Primes: 2, 3, 5, 7, 11, 13, 17, 19, 23, 29, 31, 37, 41, 43, 47, 53, 59, 61, 67, 71, 73, 79, 83, 89, 97

Prime Factors of Natural Numbers (page 21)

1. $2 \times 3 \times 11$
2. $5 \times 5 \times 13$
3. prime
4. 11×41
5. $2 \times 13 \times 19$
6. prime
7. 1. Because a prime has only itself and 1 as a factor, neither prime can be a factor of the other.

Using Prime Factors to Find the GCF (page 22)

1. GCF = 35
($245 = 5 \times 7 \times 7$,
$105 = 3 \times 5 \times 7$)

2. GCF = 165
($330 = 2 \times 3 \times 5 \times 11$,
$495 = 3 \times 3 \times 5 \times 11$,
$825 = 3 \times 5 \times 5 \times 11$)

3. GCF = 72
($792 = 2 \times 2 \times 2 \times 3 \times 11$,
$144 = 2 \times 2 \times 2 \times 3 \times 3 \times 2$,
$72 = 2 \times 2 \times 2 \times 3 \times 3$)

4. GCF = 209
($1{,}463 = 7 \times 11 \times 19$,
$1{,}045 = 5 \times 11 \times 19$)

5. GCF = 29
($899 = 29 \times 31$,
$1{,}015 = 29 \times 5 \times 7$)

6. GCF = 1 (all prime)

Prime Factors and the LCM (page 23)

1. LCM = 735
($35 = 5 \times 7$,
$245 = 5 \times 7 \times 7$,
$105 = 3 \times 5 \times 7$)

2. LCM = 9,240
($40 = 2 \times 2 \times 2 \times 5$,
$210 = 2 \times 3 \times 5 \times 7$,
$165 = 3 \times 5 \times 11$)

3. LCM = 84,150
($30 = 2 \times 3 \times 5$,
$99 = 3 \times 3 \times 11$,
$425 = 5 \times 5 \times 17$)

4. LCM = 690
($46 = 23 \times 2$,
$69 = 23 \times 3$
$115 = 23 \times 5$)

5. LCM = 42,875
($343 = 7 \times 7 \times 7$,
$125 = 5 \times 5 \times 5$,
$1{,}225 = 7 \times 7 \times 5 \times 5$)

6. LCM = 176, 715
($315 = 3 \times 3 \times 5 \times 7$,
$5{,}049 = 3 \times 3 \times 3 \times 11 \times 17$,
$561 = 3 \times 11 \times 17$)

7. The LCM would be the product of the three primes because they do not have any common prime factors.

Vocabulary Review (page 24)

1. set
2. starting at 0
3. whole number
4. decimal
5. digit
6. 1
7. that are whole, both positive and negative
8. rational
9. irrational
10. addition
11. subtraction
12. multiplication
13. division
14. divisible
15. factors
16. multiple
17. 1, the number itself
18. Common Factor
19. GCF
20. Common Multiple

Looking Back (page 25)

1. 1
2. 1
3. 2, 3, 4, 5, 6, 7, 9, 10 (7 requires a check long hand)
4. 2, 3, 4, 5, 6, 8, 9, 10
5. 29
6. 72
7. Possible Answer: 10, 20
8. Possible Answer: 2, 5
9. Possible Answer: 7
10. $2 \times 3 \times 5 \times 11$
11. GCF = 21 ($525 = 3 \times 5 \times 5 \times 7$, $693 = 3 \times 3 \times 7 \times 11$)
12. GCF = 84 ($420 = 2 \times 2 \times 3 \times 5 \times 7$, $252 = 2 \times 2 \times 3 \times 3 \times 7$)

Terminating and Repeating Decimals (page 26)

Terminating

1/2 = 0.5	1/4 = 0.25
1/5 = 0.2	1/8 = 0.125
1/10 = 0.1	3/4 = 0.75
2/5 = 0.4	3/8 = 0.375
3/10 = 0.3	3/5 = 0.6
5/8 = 0.625	

Repeating

1/3 = $0.\overline{3}$	1/6 = $0.\overline{6}$
1/7 = $0.\overline{142857}$	1/9 = $0.\overline{1}$
2/3 = $0.\overline{6}$	5/6 = $0.\overline{33}$
2/7 = $0.\overline{285714}$	5/7 = $0.\overline{714285}$
2/9 = $0.\overline{2}$	7/9 = $0.\overline{7}$
6/7 = $0.\overline{857142}$	4/9 = $0.\overline{4}$
8/9 = $0.\overline{8}$	

Fractions to Decimals (page 27)

1. L
2. A
3. D
4. B
5. C
6. E
7. H
8. G
9. J
10. K
11. I
12. F

Line It Up! (page 28)

1. 236.26
2. 4.323
3. 8.03
4. 6.58
5. 0.0835
6. 0.079
7. 1.279
8. 0.14
9. 13.58
10. 4.2
11. 88.2673
12. 2.67
13. 0.66572
14. 0.03

Multiplying with Decimals (page 29)

1. 45
2. 4.829724
3. 12.15
4. 7.2
5. 0.001675
6. 9.21
7. 16.105
8. 0.0024
9. 113.832
10. 0.1
11. 3,269.6024
12. 35.1384
13. 28,340
14. 6

Dividing with Decimals (page 30)

1. 2
2. 30
3. 100
4. 500
5. 9,000
6. 69
7. 2
8. 25.2
9. 54.32
10. 100,000
11. 600
12. 2,810
13. 66,054.3
14. 200,000

Multiples of Ten (page 31)

1. 7,890
2. 6.54
3. 5,670
4. 0.5643
5. 547,000
6. 0.1
7. 0.00199
8. 0.0034
9. 24,587.6
10. 7.892
11. 576,980
12. 7.63
13. 9,080,050
14. 7.654
15. 1
16. 0.2222
17. 505
18. 0.87965456
19. 700
20. 0.00003456005

Rounding (page 32)

1. 12.3 (down)
2. 3.035 (up)
3. 7.79 (up)
4. 2.1567 (down)
5. 3.45 (down)
6. 9.0 (down)
7. 3.674 (down)
8. 315.697 (down)
9. 654.15 (up)
10. 0 (down)
11. 1.63 (up)
12. 99 (up)
13. 6 (down)
14. 4 (up)

Mix It Up! (page 33)

1. E
2. C
3. B
4. D
5. A

6. 6.8
7. 9.54
8. 3.6248
9. 2.460

10. 342.379
11. 7.634
12. 1.5433
13. 1.207
14. 2.7
15. 5.25
16. 5,670,321
17. 8.2
18. 50.4
19. 75,400.9
20. 5.674
21. 65.454

Understanding Rational Numbers (page 34)

1.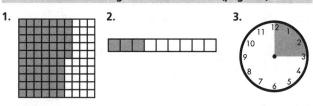
2.
3.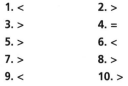

4.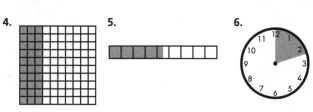
5.
6.

7.
8.
9.

Number Representations (page 35)

1.
2.

3. Possible Answer:

5. 3/4

6.

7. Answers will vary.

Comparing Fractions (page 36)

1. <
2. >
3. >
4. =
5. <
6. >
7. >
8. <
9. =
10. >

Comparing Small and Large Decimals (page 37)

1. <
2. >
3. >
4. =
5. >
6. <
7. >
8. >
9. <
10. >
11. >
12. <

Number Lines (page 38)

1.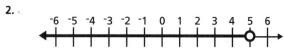
2.
3.
4.
5.
6.
7.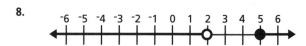
8.

Negative Numbers: + and – (page 39)

1. ⁻5
2. ⁻1
3. ⁻9
4. ⁻5
5. ⁻10
6. 24
7. ⁻14
8. ⁻14
9. 2
10. ⁻16
11. ⁻80
12. 50

Negative Numbers: × and ÷ (page 40)

1. ⁻45	**2.** 49
3. 50	**4.** 1/2
5. ⁻20	**6.** ⁻2
7. ⁻24	**8.** ⁻1
9. 48	**10.** 5
11. 250	**12.** ⁻120

Watch Out! (page 41)

1. 348	**2.** 7.63
3. ⁻12	**4.** ⁻928
5. ⁻2.7	**6.** 5.25
7. ⁻3,610,321	**8.** 8.2
9. ⁻50.4	**10.** ⁻75,400.9
11. 5.674	**12.** ⁻65.454

Finding Absolute Value (page 42)

1. 4	**2.** 5
3. 4	**4.** 4
5. ⁻7	**6.** ⁻7
7. 0	**8.** 4
9. 24	**10.** 16
11. 20	**12.** 2
13. 10	**14.** 26
15. 6	**16.** ⁻44
17. 61	**18.** 24

Adding and Subtracting Like Fractions (page 43)

1. 1/8	**2.** 1 1/2
3. 1/6	**4.** 3/8
5. 1	**6.** 1 2/5
7. 1/3	**8.** 2/3
9. 1/2	

Adding and Subtracting Unlike Fractions (page 44)

1. 1 1/24	**2.** 3/40	**3.** 1/30
4. 11/24	**5.** 11/15	**6.** 1 1/20
7. 7/24	**8.** 4/63	**9.** 6/7
10. 19/27	**11.** 4/35	**12.** 1/18
13. 1 5/6	**14.** 10/27	**15.** 11/16

Multiplying Fractions (page 45)

1. 2/9	**2.** 1/12
3. 1	**4.** 1/5
5. 1/8	**6.** 1/28
7. 1/3	**8.** 1/5
9. 200/243	**10.** 1 2/3
11. 11	**12.** 7 1/2
13. 21/256	**14.** 17 1/16

Finding Reciprocals (page 46)

1. 3/1	**2.** 3/2
3. 8/1	**4.** 6/5
5. 7/2	**6.** 9/4
7. 8/9	**8.** 11/9
9. 1/6	**10.** 1
11. 1/100	**12.** ⁻3/2
13. ⁻8/9	**14.** ⁻11/10
15. ⁻1/5	**16.** none

Dividing with Fractions (page 47)

1. 2	**2.** 1 1/2
3. 2 1/2	**4.** 25
5. 1/20	**6.** ⁻18
7. 3 1/5	**8.** ⁻1/100
9. 5/28	**10.** ⁻4
11. ⁻1/24	**12.** ⁻1
13. 1/8	**14.** ⁻1/10000
15. 1 7/20	**16.** 3 1/9

Mental Models of Dividing Fractions (page 48)

Models will vary.

1. 3	**2.** 3 1/2
3. 15	**4.** 36

Ordering Decimals (page 49)

1. ⁻3, ⁻2.5, ⁻2.2, ⁻1, ⁻0.5, 0   **2.** 3.3, 3.35, 3.4, 3.43, 3.45

3. ⁻1.1, ⁻0.65, ⁻0.55, ⁻0.5, ⁻0.45, ⁻0.05, ⁻0.01

4. 4.5, 3.35, 3.1, 3.0, 2.6, 2.2   **5.** 2.8, 2.3, 2, 1, ⁻1.5, ⁻1.6, ⁻5

6. 1.15, 0.8, 0.5, 0, ⁻0.7, ⁻1.3, ⁻1.5

Percents (page 50)

1. 0.45, 9/20

2. 2.1, 2 1/10

3. 0.004, 4/1000 or 1/250

4. 12.3%, 123/1000

5. 30%, 0.3

6. 33 1/3%, 0.$\overline{33}$

7. 12.5%, 1/8

8. 0.01, 1/100

9. 9 1/11%, 0.$\overline{09}$

10. 0.14, 7/50

11. 87.5%, 0.875

12. 67%, 0.$\overline{66}$

13. 17%, 1/6

14. 25%, 1/4

Percent Perfection (page 51)

1. 25% **2.** 25% **3.** 33% **4.** 50%

Models will vary.

5. (1/4 shaded)

6. (1 whole and 1/4 shaded)

7. (2/100 shaded)

8. Possible Answer: If you divided 4 cups into 100 equal parts, then Johnny ate 4 parts. This is a small amount, and it is possible.

9. Randy got an additional 7 correct. This is possible. He would then have 9 out of 10 correct.

10. More than all of the calls will be cheaper. This is not possible.

11. Maggie read 1 of every 1,000 books in her library. If the library is not large and Maggie has a lot of time, this is possible.

Ordering Decimals, Percents, and Fractions (page 52)

1. 5, 5 1/4, 5.5, 560%

2. ⁻4 1/2, ⁻4, 0, 4, 435%

3. 1/4, 35%, 0.4, 1/2

4. ⁻2, 0.2, 25%, 2/3, 1 1/8

5. ⁻4.8, ⁻2 3/4, ⁻2.55, ⁻2 1/2, ⁻2.45

6. 61%, 2/3, 0.7, 3/4

Money (page 53)

1. $0.26, 26¢

2. (money adding up to $2.50), 250¢

3. (money adding up to $0.99), $0.99

4. $3.05, 305¢

5. (money adding up to $5), $5.00

6. (money adding up to $1.99), 199¢

Cents and Dollars (page 54)

1. No coin. 99/100 of a penny is less than 1 penny.

2. 99¢ means 99 pennies or 99 cents and 0.99¢ is a little less than 1 penny.

3. Answers will vary.

4. Possible Answers: With interest smaller than 1¢; when figuring out the cost per item when you paid $1 for 3 items.

Discounts (page 55)

1. $27.20 **2.** $56.25 **3.** $5.40

4. $25.20 **5.** $6 **6.** $37.50

7. $2 **8.** $28 **9.** $157.35

10. No, it is less than 55%. Possible Answer: 30% off $100 is $70.00. 25% off $70 is $52.50. 55% off $100 is $45.00. $45.00 < $52.50

Working with Coins (page 56)

Coin A = 25¢

Coin B = 1¢

Coin C = 5¢

Coin D = 10¢

Rational Numbers (page 57)

Across	Down
1. denominator	**1.** dollars
2. numerator	**3.** reciprocals
6. percent	**4.** cents
7. absolute value	**5.** repeating decimals

Vocabulary Scramble (page 58)

1. repeating decimals

2. terminating decimals

3. denominator

4. numerator

5. less than

6. greater than

7. absolute value

8. reciprocal

9. percent

"Write a definition for each of the above vocabulary words."

Rational Review 1 (page 59)

1. 127.356

2. ⁻8

3. ⁻18

4. 6

5. 5/6

6. 3/8

7. 21/40

8. ⁻1 1/5

9. 1/9, 0.15, 0.2, 0.3, 1/3

10. 1/7, 1/6, 1/5, 1/4, 1/2

11. (70 small boxes shaded)

12. (1 and 1/2 shaded circles)

13. >

14. >

15. multiply by 3 on both sides

16. 0.007

17. 1 9/20

18. 1/4

19. $0.55

20. 6/5

Rational Review 2 (page 60)

1. 782.3345
2. 6
3. 36
4. ⁻6
5. 2/15
6. 1 1/15
7. ⁻1/8
8. 1 4/5
9. 1/11, 0.1, 1/8, 0.13, 0.2
10. 1/9, 1/8, 1/6, 1/4, 1/3
11. (3 of the 10 parts shaded)
12. (3 shaded circles)
13. >
14. =
15. divide by 5 on both sides
16. 0.205
17. 3
18. 100%
19. 99¢
20. 3

Ratios and Rates (page 61)

1. Rate: 4 pieces per student
2. Rate: 20 points per player
3. Ratio: 9 to 8 doctors
4. Ratio: 35 seconds for each minute
5. Rate: 8 seeds per pot
6. Ratio: 10 beads for each bead
7. Rate: 50 stars per flag
8. Ratio: 2 minutes for each 3 hours
9. Ratio: 5 pencils for each student
10. Ratio: 1:20 or 1/20
11. Ratio: 1:3 or 1/3
12. Rate: 1:6 or 1/6

Company Comparisons (page 62)

1. Answers will vary.

Company A	Company B	Company C	Company D
$0.20 $0.20/min	$0.50 $0.50/min	$0.25 $0.25/min	$5 $5/min
$1 $0.20/min	$1.10 $0.22/min	$1.25 $0.25/min	$5 $1/min
$2 $0.20/min	$1.85 18.5¢/min	$2.50 $0.25/min	$5 $0.50/min
$6 $0.20/min	$4.85 $0.16/min	$4.80 $0.16/min	$5 $0.17/min
$12 $0.20/min	$9.35 15.5¢/min	$7.80 $0.13/min	$5 $0.08/min
$20 $0.20/min	$15.35 5¢/min	$11.80 12¢/min	$5 $0.05/min

2. Answers will vary.

Comparing Rates (page 63)

1. A
2. A
3. B
4. C
5. D
6. D

7. Possible Answer:

	PROS	CONS
Company A	Cheap short calls, easy to understand	No discount for long calls
Company B	Good rate after about 5–10 minutes	Connection fee is expensive for short calls
Company C	Discount for long calls	Expensive short calls
Company D	Very cheap for long calls	If an answering machine picks up, you will have to pay $5

Using Powers and Square Roots (page 64)

1. 1
2. 64
3. 3
4. 16
5. 3
6. 4
7. 9
8. 6

9. Six to the seventh power or Six to the power of seven
10. Square root of 16
11. Three squared

Value Chart (page 65)

x	x^2	$\sqrt{x^2}$
1	1	1
2	4	2
3	9	3
4	16	4
5	25	5
6	36	6
7	49	7
8	64	8
9	81	9
10	100	10

Order of Operations (page 66)

1. 10.5
2. 41
3. 21
4. 58
5. ⁻12
6. 11
7. 11
8. 7
9. 50
10. 47
11. ⁻44
12. 218 3/4

Take the Challenge (page 67)

1. 16
2. 3
3. 4
4. 3
5. 4
6. 4
7. $(7 + 3) \div 5 \times 2 + 3 = 7$
8. $7 + 3 \div 5 \times (2 + 3) = 10$
9. (no parentheses needed)
10. $(2 + 3)^2 + (3 + 1)^2 = 41$
11. (no parentheses needed)
12. $2 + 3^2 + (3 + 1)^2 = 27$
13. false = 9
14. false = 37.5
15. true
16. false = 400

Estimating (page 68)

1. False. 5/6 is less than 1.
2. False. 1/3 is less than 0.5.
3. False. 3/4 + 1/3 would be more than 1. 9/10 is less than 1.
4. False. 1/6 + 1/5 would be less than 1/2.
5. True. 4/5 + 1/4 would be more than 1.
6. True. 5/6 + 1/5 would be more than 1.
7. True: 1/2 + 1/3 + 1/6 would equal 1.
8. True: 1/9 + 1/4 would be less than 1/2.
9. True. The popcorn and drink would be less than $6.
10. False. The price is too high. It should be $7.

Mental Math (page 69)

1. $5   actual
2. $3.60   estimate
3. $6   actual
4. $3.50   actual
5. $23   estimate
6. Possible Answer: Kristina has plenty of time.
7. Possible Answer: Even if the items were priced at the high end, the $90 Michael has is enough.

Understanding Large Numbers (page 70)

1. 5.43×10^6
2. 2.10×10^8
3. 9.99×10^5
4. 6.78×10^9
5. 345,000,000
6. 70,000,000,000
7. 5,432,000,000
8. 21,230
9. Thirty-two times ten to the power of ten
10. Four and fifty-six hundredths times ten to the eighth power

Teeny-Tiny! (page 71)

1. 5.46×10^{-5}
2. 9.832×10^{-5}
3. 1.357×10^{-2}
4. 3.0001×10^{-4}
5. 5×10^{-7}
6. 5.4321×10^{-5}
7. 0.0000000145
8. 0.00000000061
9. 0.00000003
10. 0.000050041
11. 0.0000020005
12. 0.004321

Multiplying Extreme Numbers (page 72)

1. 7.2×10^{16}
2. 2.05×10^{-7}
3. 7.75
4. 7.4151×10^4
5. 12.6×10^{11}
6. 2.492×10^4
7. 1.34
8. 5.4×10^{-3}
9. 1.8
10. 2.4854×10

Putting It Together (page 73)

1. same units of measure
2. different units of measure
3. ratios
4. power
5. two
6. the number
7. order of operations
8. close

9. rate
10. 12
11. 7 or ⁻7
12. 32
13. 1

14. 2.34×10^6
15. 5×10^{-5}
16. 1.17×10^2

Additional Practice (page 74)

1. power
2. square
3. square root
4. order of operations
5. rate
6. ratio
7. scientific notation
8. estimate

9. ratio (160 inches/168 inches)
10. 63
11. 12 or ⁻12
12. 64
13. 7

14. 1.234×10^7
15. 3×10^{-5}
16. 3.702×10^2

Understanding Variables (page 75)

1. $2 = p \times s$
2. $(9)(5) = x$
3. $D = 2r$
4. $s = 12m$
5. $s = b + 2$
6. $As = L^2$
7. $30/u = r$
8. $H = x \div 60$
9. $Ps = 4L$
10. $Pr = 2(L + w)$

Equations with Variables (page 76)

Answers may vary.

1. $G = B + 2$
2. $V = 5 + 6$
3. $D = 10 - 5$
4. $M = 100 - 2$
5. $D = 1 + 2 + 3 + 4 + 5 + 6$
6. $C = T/S$
7. $Ps = Po - Pd$
8. $T = 500 \times 1.06$
9. $Tb = N \times Tp$
10. $Sn = Ss(n/Ss)$

Common Algebra Terms (page 77)

$4y - 5x \bullet 7 + 3y$	$x + 2x + 3x + 4x$	$3 \bullet 4 - 6y + 2y + x + 2x$
$-, \bullet, +$	$+ \bullet$	$-, \bullet, +$
y, x	x	x, y
$4y, ⁻5x , 7 , 3y$	x, 2x, 3x, 4x	3, 4, ⁻6y, 2y, x, 2x
4y and 3y	all	3 and 4, ⁻6y and 2y, x and 2x
4, ⁻5, 7, 3	1, 2, 3, 4	3, 4, ⁻6, 2, 1, 2

Write It! (page 78)

Variables may differ in the formulas below.

1. The (total pay) is the product of (hours worked) and (hourly rate.) **P = H × R**

2. The (interest earned) is equal to the (principal) multiplied by the (interest rate) multiplied by the (time.) **I = PRT**

3. The (distance) is equal to the product of the (rate of speed) and (time.) **D = R × T**

4. The (weight of the cat) is the difference of the (weight of the dog) and (twenty pounds.) **C = |D − 20|**

5. The (cost) of one candy bar is equal to (one dollar) divided by (two.) **C = $1 ÷ 2**

6. The (y-value) is equal to the product of the (slope) and (x-value) and then added to the (y-intercept.) **Y = mx + b**

7. The (square of x) is equal to (x) multiplied by (x.) **S = x • x**

8. The (area of a circle) is equal to (pi) times the (radius) squared. **A = πr²**

9. The (length of the hypotenuse) squared equals the sum of (each side) squared. **H² = a² + b²**

10. The (number of students receiving an A) on the test was equal to (15%) of the total (number of students.) **A = 0.15 • S**

Investigation (page 79)

Models will vary.

1. 6x + 9y + 7
2. 7x + 5y + 10
3. 12x + 10y
4. 7x + 5y + 10
5. 12x + 6y + 12
6. $30x^2 + 27$
7. ⁻16 x + 10y + 29
8. $20x^2 + 40y^2$

Distribute It! (page 80)

1. 1,190	2. 5x + 20
3. 6x + 6y	4. 5x + 5y + 500
5. 30x + 10z + 120	6. 12a + 9b
7. 2a + b	8. 8x
9. 8x + 3	10. 10x + 5

Adding Like Terms (page 81)

1. 5a
2. 8y + 3
3. 3p + 8z + 5
4. 13r + 6
5. 14x
6. 18b
7. 11x + 7y
8. 30x + 16y + 13
9. 44a + 23
10. 31x + 41y + 6
11. 26x + 26y + 14z
12. 82x + 77y + 55z
13. 24x + 35y + 27z + 30
14. 33x + 30y + 15z + 12

Simplify It! (page 82)

1. 13y
2. 7a
3. 4x
4. ⁻2a + 2b
5. 7x + 4y
6. 26x – y –11
7. f + 5z + 6
8. 5x + 5y
9. 6a + 13
10. 22x – 7y + 31z
11. 12x + 9y
12. ⁻4a + 8

Evaluate (page 83)

1.	⁻2	2	⁻1/2
2.	10	⁻22	⁻2
3.	6	⁻6	1 1/2
4.	3	⁻3	3/4
5.	1	1	1
6.	5 2/3	4 1/3	5 1/6
7.	⁻5	0.5	1/8
8.	0	0	0
9.	8	8	8
10.	46	22	37

Equations and Solutions (page 84)

1. is a solution
2. is not a solution
3. is a solution
4. is not a solution
5. is a solution
6. is not a solution
7. is a solution
8. is not a solution
9. is not a solution
10. is a solution
11. is a solution
12. is not a solution
13. is not a solution
14. is not a solution
15. is not a solution

Undoing (page 85)

1. E
2. G
3. J
4. F
5. C
6. K
7. B
8. D
9. L
10. I
11. A
12. H

More to Undo (page 86)

1. add 2
2. divide by 3
3. multiply by 2
4. multiply by 2
5. subtract ⁻2 or add 2
6. subtract
   add
   divide
   multiply
7. multiply by 2, $a/2 \times 2 = 4 \times 2$, $a = 8$
8. divide by 3, $a \times 3 \div 3 = 12 \div 3$, $a = 4$
9. divide by 5 , $a \times 5 \div 5 = 6 \div 5$, $a = 6/5$

Solving Equations with Addition (page 87)

1. $a = 1$	2. $x = 13$	3. $z = 39$
4. $b = 8$	5. $y = 7$	6. $x = 2$
7. $y = ⁻2$	8. $z = 10$	9. $a = ⁻2$

Subtraction Solutions (page 88)

1. $a = 11$	2. $x = 30$
3. $z = 31$	4. $b = 20$
5. $y = 25$	6. $x = 24$
7. $y = 2$	8. $z = 10$

Multiplication Solutions (page 89)

1. $a = 2$	2. $x = 2$
3. $z = 4$	4. $b = 4$
5. $y = 8$	6. $x = 5$
7. $y = 12/5$	8. $z = ⁻6/4$

Division Solutions (page 90)

1. $a = 12$	2. $x = 20$
3. $z = 33$	4. $b = 28$
5. $y = 72$	6. $x = 30$
7. $y = ⁻8$	8. $z = ⁻12$

All Together (page 91)

1. $y = ⁻32$	2. $x = 2$
3. $a = 25$	4. $y = ⁻5$
5. $y = ⁻392$	6. $y = ⁻4$
7. $b = ⁻3$	8. $y = ⁻144$
9. $z = ⁻2$	10. $a = 6$
11. $y = 6/5$	12. $x = 1/3$
13. $x = 5$	14. $x = 7$
15. $x = 8$	16. $x = 2$

Educational Equations (page 92)

1. 1	2. 9
3. 2	4. 3
5. 7	6. 4
7. 8	8. 5
9. 6	

"Education is not received… IT IS ACHIEVED."

Proportions (page 93)

1. $a = 4$	2. $d = 12$
3. $c = 1$	4. $x = 18$
5. $b = 4$	6. $d = 20$
7. $b = 8$	8. $a = 3$
9. $a = 4$	10. $d = 8$
11. $x = 45$	12. $x = 35$

Advanced Proportions (page 94)

1. $d = 4.5$	2. $b = 10$	3. $b = 4$
4. $c = 8$	5. $a = 2$	6. $a = 1$
7. $d = 15$	8. $d = 24$	9. $x = 75$
10. $a = 48$	11. $x = 5$	12. $a = 6$

Discovery (page 95)

1. True
2. True
3. False
4. False
5. True
6. True
7. False
8. False
9. True
10. True
11. False
12. False
13. True
14. True
15. False
16. False

Associative and Commutative Properties (page 96)

1. Commutative Property of Addition
2. Associative Property of Addition
3. Disprove; Example: $3 - 2 = 1 \neq 2 - 3 = ⁻1$
4. Disprove; Example: $(4 - 3) - 2 = ⁻1 \neq 4 - (3 - 2) = 3$
5. Commutative Property of Multiplication
6. Associative Property of Multiplication
7. Disprove; Example: $49 \div 7 = 7 \neq 7 \div 49 = 1/7$
8. Disprove; Example: $(10 \div 5) \div 2 = 1 \neq 10 \div (5 \div 2) = 4$

Shortcuts (page 97)

1. a^9
2. b^8
3. y^{12}
4. z^{25}
5. a^{24}
6. b^7
7. a^{13}
8. y^{10}
9. b^9
10. a^{20}
11. a
12. a^9
13. 1
14. y^5

15. $>$
16. $>$
17. $<$
18. $=$

Division Property of Exponents (page 98)

1. a^3
2. b^2
3. y
4. b^4
5. y^2
6. z^3
7. a^7
8. y^4
9. z^6
10. b^{21}
11. a^4
12. 1
13. a^4
14. $a^2 \div y^{-3}$

15. 16
16. 3
17. 1
18. 4.5

Simplifying Polynomials (page 99)

1. not standard: $x^6 + x^3 + x^2$
2. standard
3. not standard: $2x^7 + x^5 + 4x^2 + 3x + 5$
4. not standard: $3x^9 + x^8 + x^5 + 3x^3 + 4x + 5$
5. standard
6. not standard: $50x^6 + 3x^3 + 12x^2 + 100$
7. not standard: $5x^4 + 5x^3 + 5x^2 + 5x + 5$
8. standard
9. not standard: $x^7 + 4x^4 + 4x^3 + 12$
10. not standard: $5x^6 + 2x^5 + 27$

Monomials, Binomials, and Trinomials (page 100)

1. Monomial
2. Trinomial
3. Monomial
4. Monomial
5. Trinomial
6. Binomial
7. Monomial
8. Trinomial
9. Binomial
10. Monomial

More Polynomials (page 101)

1. $5x^3 + 2x^2 + 13$
   Trinomial
2. $6z$
   Monomial
3. $3b + 7$
   Binomial
4. z
   Monomial
5. $z^2 + 6$
   Binomial
6. $2a^3 + 11a$
   Binomial
7. $3x^3 + 4x^2$
   Binomial
8. $22y^3 + 30y^2$
   Binomial
9. $11x + 6$
   Binomial
10. $^-20y^3 - 30y^2 + 8$
    Trinomial
11. $9x^3 + 2x^2 + 14$
    Trinomial
12. $18a^3 + 12a + 10$
    Trinomial
13. $5x^3 + 4x^2$
    Binomial
14. $29y^4 + 48y^3$
    Binomial
15. $x^2 + 9x + 16$
    Trinomial
16. $^-40x^2 - 60y^2 + 4$
    Trinomial

Evaluating Simple Expressions (page 102)

1. 1
2. $^-5$
3. 10
4. $^-7$ 2/3
5. $^-7$
6. 8
7. 8
8. $^-29$
9. 36
10. 40
11. 58
12. 35

Crossword Vocabulary Review (page 103)

Across
2. proportion
5. solution
7. like terms
8. variable
10. equation
11. expression
12. inverse

Down
1. terms
2. polynomial
3. operations
4. coefficients
6. simplified
9. open sentences

Algebra Basics (page 104)

1. The (number of A grades) is $\boxed{5}$ less than the (number of B grades) in the class. **A = B − 5**

2. The (exterior angle) of a triangle is the sum of the (two nonadjacent interior angles.) **E = A + B**

3. Associative Property of Addition
4. Disprove Example: $4 - 3 \neq 3 - 4$
5. Commutative Property of Multiplication
6. Distributive; $5x + 20$
7. $y = {}^-32$
8. $x = 2$
9. $a = 8$
10. $8y^5 + 6y$ Binomial
11. z^6 Monomial
12. $11a + 10$ Binomial
13. ${}^-20y^3 - 30y^2 + 8$ Trinomial
14. 12
15. 4
16. ${}^-6$

More Algebra Basics (page 105)

1. The (volume) of a cube is the (length of one side) to the $\boxed{third}$ power. **V = S³**

2. The (sale price) is the (original price) multiplied by the difference of the (discount %) and $\boxed{100\%}$ **S = P(100% − D%)**

3. Disprove Example: $(5 - 4) - 3 \neq 5 - (4 - 3)$
4. Commutative Property of Multiplication
5. Disprove Example: $49 \div 7 \neq 7 \div 49$
6. Distributive Property; $11x + 11$ or $11(x + 1)$
7. $y = 3$
8. $x = 15$
9. $a = 27/10$ or $2\ 7/10$
10. $y^5 + y$ Binomial
11. z^{10} Monomial
12. $100a^6$ Monomial
13. $6y^3 + y^2 + 15$ Trinomial
14. 1
15. ${}^-5$
16. 10

Reciprocals (page 106)

1. 66	2. ${}^-48$
3. 160	4. 45
5. ${}^-84$	6. 48
7. ${}^-13.5$	8. 15
9. $1\ 7/8$	10. 8
11. 1	12. 8

Complex Equations (page 107)

1. 9	2. 1
3. 3	4. 4
5. 6	6. 3
7. 4	8. ${}^-8$
9. 3	10. ${}^-2$
11. 1/7	12. 2

More Complex Equations (page 108)

1. ${}^-.25$	2. 9
3. 8	4. 3
5. 20	6. 12
7. 5	8. 5
9. 2	10. 15
11. 12	12. 0
13. 10	14. 16
15. 8	16. 8
17. 8	18. 8
19. 8	20. 1

Isolating Variables 1 (page 109)

1. ${}^-42$	2. 1/6
3. ${}^-3$	4. 8
5. ${}^-6$	6. 2
7. 10	8. ${}^-8$
9. 7	10. 6
11. 3	12. $2.\overline{6}$

Isolating Variables 2 (page 110)

1. ${}^-16$	2. 4
3. 6	4. 5
5. 2	6. 10
7. ${}^-7$	8. ${}^-1$
9. 9	10. 9
11. 5	12. 5.5

Multiple Transformations (page 111)

1. is not a solution
2. is a solution
3. is a solution
4. is not a solution

5. ${}^-10$
6. 13
7. $1\ 6/7$
8. ${}^-5$
9. 1/2

Advanced Concepts (page 112)

1. 50
2. 5/6
3. 8

4. 2
5. 1
6. ⁻2
7. ⁻2
8. ⁻3
9. cancels out to 0 = 0

10. is a solution
11. is a solution
12. is a solution

You Choose 1 (page 113)

Answers will vary.

You Choose 2 (page 114)

Answers will vary.